Contractions.

Av., Avoir.	=Avoirdupois.	HP	=Horsepower.
bk.	=Book.	in., ins.	=Inch, Inches.
Brit.	=British.	k.,kg.,kilos.	=Kilograms
c. cu. cub.	=Cube.	km.	=Kilometres.
cc.	=Cubic centimetres.	lb., lbs.	=Pound, pounds.
ctl.	=Cental.	lit.	=Litres
chns.	=Chains.	m., mt., met.	=Metres.
cm.	=Centimetres.	mgs.	=Milligrams.
cwt.	=Hundredweight.	mm.	=Millimetres.
dcm.	=Decimetres.	mn.	=Minims.
Dec.	=Decimal.	ozs.	=Ounce, ounces.
drs.	=Drams.	pls.	=Poles.
fl.	=Fluid.	pts.	=Pints.
fr.	=Fraction.	q., qrs.	=Quarters.
ft.	=Foot, feet.	qtls.	=Quintals.
gall.	=Gallon.	Sq.	=Square.
gm.	=Grams.	Tnn.	=Tonne.
grs.	=Grains.	yd., yds.	=Yard, yards.

(Brit.-Met. and Met.-Brit.)

UNITED STATES Supplement, see pp. 93-100.

THE 'EXPRESS'

BRITISH INTO METRIC

CONVERSION TABLES

For Kilos, Grammes, Litres, Hectolitres;
Metres (Lineal, Square, and Cube); Millimetres
&c.

BY
J. GALL INGLIS, F.R.S.E.
Compiler of the 'Ideal' Ready Reckoner, 'Express'
Percentage Reckoner, &c.

POIDS ET MESURES ANGLAIS
Convertis en poids et mesures métriques
ENGLISCHE GEWICHTE UND MASSE
Zu metrischen umgerechnet
PESI E MISURE INGLESI
Convertiti in pesi e misure metrici
PESOS Y MEDIDAS INGLESAS
Convertidas al sistema métrico

A Metric-British Volume is also Issued.

GALL & INGLIS
12 NEWINGTON ROAD, EDINBURGH, 9
AND LONDON

PREFACE.

THIS book, with its companion volume, has been prepared to expedite the work of exporters and importers in dealing with the metric weights and measures most frequently used commercially. The delicate measurements required in engineering have also been provided for.

It is so designed as to give a very great range of equivalents with the minimum of trouble, the large numbers being frequently repeated on every leaf to obviate the necessity for referring to another page if any adding is required. Thus the equivalent of 9 tonnes, 949 kilogrammes, requires two readings only, at the same opening.

The calculations are based on the present legal British equivalents, as fixed by Order in Council, May 1908, given on page iii., but as some of these are only convenient approximations, suitable for small numbers, multiples of the larger numbers are usually based on a more exact value, derived from the highly detailed equivalents fixed for the metre, kilogram, &c.

The equivalents are sometimes given to smaller fractions than is really required for ordinary commercial purposes, but this has the advantage of giving very exact values where multiples by 10, 100, &c. are desired, by shifting the decimal point.

The calculations have been made with great care and have been carefully checked. Typographical errors have been eradicated as far as possible by three readings of the proofs.

EDINBURGH,   J. G. I.

DICTIONARY.

Britain	Français	Italiano	Español	Deutsch
Apothecaries'	des apothicaires	pesi da farmacisti	apotecarios	apothekergewicht
Atmosphere	atmosphère	atmosfera	atmósfera	atmosphäre
Capacity	capacité	capacità	capacidad	aufnahmevermogen
Contractions	contractions	contrazioni	contracciones	abkürzungen
Cube	cubique	cubico	cúbico	kubik-
Decimals ..	décimales	decimali	decimales	dezimale
Equivalents	equivalents	equivalenti	equivalentes	äquivalent
Fluid	fluide	fluido	fluido	flüssigkeit
Horsepower	HP(cheval-vapeur)	HP(cavallo vapora)	caballos de fuerza	pferdekraft
Index ..	index	indice	indice	inhaltsverzeichnis
Into	en	in	al	zu
Legal ..	légale	legale	legal	gesetzliches
Lineal ..	linéaire	lineare	lineal	längen-
Liquid ..	liquide	liquido	líquido	flüssig
Measure ..	mesure	misure	medida	mass
Metric ..	métrique	metrico	métrico	metrische
Of	de	di	de	von
Pages ..	pages	pagine	páginas	seiten
Per (⅌)	par	da	la	pro
Preface ..	préface	prefazione	introducción	einleitung
Shipping Ton	tonne maritime	tonnellata mariti-	tonelada maritima	schiffstonne
Short Ton	tonne courte	,, corta [ma	,, de 2000 lb	kleine tonne
Square ..	carré; de superficie	quadrato	cuadrado	quadrat-
Thermal Unit	unité thermale	unità termale	unidad termal	wärmeeinheit
Timber ..	bois	legno	madera	nutzholz
Water ..	eau	acqua	agua	wasser
Weight ..	poids	pesi	peso	gewicht

(*British-Metric*)

A

EQUIVALENTS.
Lineal Measure.

1 Inch	= 25·400 Millimetres.
1 Foot = 12 Inches	= 0·30480 Metre.
1 Yard = 3 Feet (36 *inches*)	= 0·914399 ,,
1 Fathom = 6 Feet (2 *yards*)	= 1·8288 Metres.
1 Pole = 5½ Yards (16½ *feet*) ...	= 5·0292 ,,
1 Chain = 100 Links (22 *yds.*: 66 *ft.*: 4 *pls.*)	= 20·1168 ,,
1 Furlong = 40 Poles (220 *yards* : 660 *feet*)	= 201·168 ,,
1 Mile = 8 Furlongs (1760 *yds.*: 5280 *ft.*) =	1·6093 Kilometres.

Square Measure.

1 Sq. Inch	= 6·4516 Sq. Centimetres.
1 Sq. Foot = 144 Square Inches ...	= 9·2903 Sq. Decimetres.
1 Sq. Yard = 9 ,, Feet (1296 *sq. ins.*) =	0·836126 Sq. Metre.
1 Perch (sq. pole)=30¼ ,, Yards (272¼ *sq. ft.*) =	25·293 Sq. Metres.
1 Sq. Chain = 16 Perches (484 *sq. yds.*) =	4·0468 Ares.
1 Rood = 40 ,, (1210 *sq. yds.*)=	10·117 ,,
1 Acre =4 Roods(10 *sq. chns.*: 4840 *sq. yds.*)=	0·40468 Hectare.
1 Sq. Mile = 640 Acres	=259·00 Hectares.

Cubic Measure.

1 Cube Inch ... =16·387 Cube Centimetres (=16·387 millilitres).
1 ,, Foot = 1728 Cube Inches ... = 0·028317 Cube Metre.
1 ,, Yard = 27 ,, Feet(46,656 *cub. ins.*)= 0·764553 ,, ,,
40 ,, Feet = 1 Shipping Ton = 1·13268 Cube Metres.
1 Petrograd Standard=165 Cube Feet (*Timber*)=4·672 ,, ,,

Liquid & Capacity Measure.

1 Gill = 5 Fluid Ozs.	= 1·42 Decilitres.
1 Pint = 4 Gills (20 *ozs. Avoir. of water*)=	0·568 Litre.
1 Quart = 2 Pints	= 1·136 Litres.
1 Gallon = 4 Quarts (10 *lbs. Avoir. of water*)=	4·5459631 Litres.
1 Peck = 2 Gallons (8 *quarts*) ...	= 9·092 Litres.
1 Bushel = 4 Pecks (8 *gallons*) ...	= 3·637 Dekalitres.
1 Quarter = 8 Bushels	= 2·909 Hectolitres.
1 Minim	= 0·059 Millilitre.
1 Fluid Drachm=60 minims(=⅛ oz.: 54·6875 *grains*)=	3·552 Millilitres.
1 Fluid Oz. (*Av.*)= 8 Fluid Drachms(16 *Av. drams*)=	2·84123 Centilitres.
1 Pint =20 Fluid Ounces (*Avoir.*)	=0·568 Litre.

'Avoirdupois' Weight.

1 Grain	= 0·0648 Gram.
1 Dram (27 11⁄32 *grains*)	= 1·772 Grams.
1 Ounce (*Avoir.*) = 16 Drams (437½ *grains*)=	28·350 ,,
1 Pound = 16 Ounces (7000 *grains*) ...	=0·45359243 Kilogr.
1 Stone (legal) = 14 Pounds	= 6·350 Kilograms.
1 Quarter = 28 Pounds (2 *stones*) ...	= 12·70 ,,
1 Cental = 100 Pounds	= 45·359 ,,
1 Hundredweight = 4 Quarters (112 *lb.*: 8 *stones*)=	50·80 ,,
1 'Short Ton' = 20 Centals (2000 *Pounds*) ...	=907·185 ,,
1 Ton (2240 *lb.*) =20 Hundredweight=1016 Kilos=	1·0160 Tonnes.

'Troy' & Apothecaries' Weight.

1 Scruple = 20 Grains	= 1·296 Grams.
1 Drachm = 3 Scruples(60 *grains*=⅛ oz. *Troy*)=	3·888 ,,
1 Ounce 'Troy'= 8 Drachms (480 *grains*) ...	= 31·1035 ,,
1 Pound 'Troy'=12 Ounces 'Troy' (5760 *grains*)=	373·242 ,,

1 British Thermal Unit (B.Th.U.) = ·252 Calories.
1 British Horse-power (HP) = 1·014 Metric Horse-power.
1 Kilowatt=1·346 British HP. = 1·36
1 Atmosphere (14·7 lb. ℔ sq.in.)=1·033 Atmospheres (Metric)=1·033 kilos ℔ sq.cm.

EQUIVALENTS.

Ozs. ℣ l. ft. (Ounces per Lineal Foot) = Grams per Lineal Metre.
Ozs. ℣ l. yd. (,, ,, ,, Yard) = ,, ,, ,, ,,
Lbs. ℣ l. ft. (Pounds per Lineal Foot) = Kilos. per Lineal Metre.
Lbs. ℣ l. yd. (,, ,, ,, Yard) = ,, ,, ,, ,,
Lb. ℣ l. mile (,, ,, ,, Mile) = ,, ,, Kilometre.

Oz. ℣ sq. ft. (Ounces per Square Foot) = Grams per Square Metre.
Oz. ℣ sq. yd. (,, ,, ,, Yard) = ,, ,, ,,

No.	ozs. ℣ l.ft. =gms.℣m. =23 gm.	ozs. ℣ l.yd. =gms.℣m. =8 gm.	lbs. ℣ l.ft. =kilos.℣m. =0·372kg	lbs. ℣ l.yd. =kilos.℣m. =0·124kg	lb. ℣ l.mile =kilos.℣ k. =·070 kg	oz.℣ sq.ft. =g.℣sq.m. =76gm.	oz.℣ sq.yd =g.℣sq.m =8·5gm.
¼							
½	47	16	0·744	0·248	0·141	153	17·0
¾	70	23	1·116	0·372	0·211	228	25·4
1	93	31	1·488	0·496	0·282	305	33·9
2	186	62	2·976	0·992	0·564	610	67·8
3	279	93	4·464	1·488	0·846	916	101·7
4	372	124	5·953	1·984	1·127	1221	135·6
5	465	155	7·441	2·480	1·409	1526	169·5
6	558	186	8·929	2·976	1·691	1831	203·4
7	651	217	10·417	3·472	1·973	2136	237·3
8	744	248	11·905	3·968	2·255	2441	271·2
9	837	279	13·393	4·464	2·537	2747	305·2
10	930	310	14·882	4·961	2·819	3052	339·1
11	1023	341	16·370	5·457	3·100	3357	373·0
12	1116	372	17·858	5·953	3·382	3662	406·9
13	1209	403	19·346	6·449	3·664	3967	440·8
14	1302	434	20·834	6·945	3·946	4272	474·7
15	1395	465	22·322	7·441	4·228	4578	508·6
16	1488	496	23·811	7·937	4·510	4883	542·5
17	1581	527	25·299	8·433	4·792	5188	576·4
18	1674	558	26·787	8·929	5·073	5493	610·3
19	1767	589	28·275	9·425	5·355	5798	644·2
20	1860	620	29·763	9·921	5·637	6103	678·1
21	1953	651	31·251	10·417	5·919	6409	712·0
22	2046	682	32·740	10·913	6·201	6714	745·9
23	2139	713	34·228	11·409	6·483	7019	779·8
24	2232	744	35·716	11·905	6·765	7324	813·7
25	2325	775	37·204	12·401	7·046	7629	847·6
26	2418	806	38·692	12·897	7·328	7934	881·6
27	2511	837	40·180	13·393	7·610	8240	915·5
28	2604	868	41·669	13·890	7·892	8545	949·4
29	2697	899	43·157	14·386	8·174	8850	983·3
30	2790	930	44·645	14·882	8·456	9155	1017·2

Lbs. ℔ sq. in. (Pounds per Square Inch) = Kilos. per Sq. Centimetre.
Lbs. ℔ sq. ft. (,, ,, ,, Foot) = ,, Square Metre.
Lbs. ℔ sq. yd. (,, ,, ,, Yard) = ,, ,, ,, ,,
Lbs. ℔ c. ft. (Pounds per Cube Foot) = Kilos per Cube Metre.
Lbs. ℔ c. yd. (,, ,, ,, Yard) = ,, ,, ,, ,,
Lbs. ℔ qr. (Pounds per Quarter) = Kilos per Hectolitre.
Lbs. ℔ bush. (,, ,, Bushel) = ,, ,, Dekalitre.

No.	lbs. ℔ sq. in. =kg. ℔ s. cm	lbs. ℔ sq. ft. =kg℔sq.m.	lbs. ℔ sq. yd. =kg℔sq.m.	lbs. ℔ c. ft. =kg. ℔ c. m.	lbs. ℔ c. yd. =kg. ℔ c. m.	lbs. ℔ qr. =kg. ℔ hect	lb℔bush k.℔ dkl
¼	0·018kg.	1·22kg.	=0·14 kg	=4·00 kg	=0·15 kg	0·039kg.	0·03 k
½	0·035	2·44	0·27	8·01	0·30	0·078	0·06
¾	0·053	3·66	0·41	12·01	0·44	0·117	0·09
1	0·070	4·88	0·54	16·02	0·59	0·156	0·12
2	0·141	9·76	1·08	32·04	1·19	0·312	0·25
3	0·211	14·65	1·63	48·06	1·78	0·468	0·37
4	0·281	19·53	2·17	64·07	2·37	0·624	0·50
5	0·352	24·41	2·71	80·09	2·97	0·780	0·62
6	0·422	29·29	3·25	96·11	3·56	0·935	0·75
7	0·492	34·18	3·80	112·13	4·15	1·091	0·87
8	0·562	39·06	4·34	128·15	4·75	1·247	1·00
9	0·633	43·94	4·88	144·17	5·34	1·403	1·12
10	0·703	48·82	5·42	160·18	5·93	1·559	1·25
11	0·773	53·71	5·97	176·20	6·53	1·715	1·37
12	0·844	58·59	6·51	192·22	7·12	1·871	1·50
13	0·914	63·47	7·05	208·24	7·71	2·027	1·62
14	0·984	68·35	7·59	224·26	8·31	2·183	1·75
15	1·055	73·24	8·14	240·28	8·90	2·339	1·87
16	1·125	78·12	8·68	256·29	9·49	2·494	2·00
17	1·195	83·00	9·22	272·31	10·09	2·650	2·12
18	1·266	87·88	9·76	288·33	10·68	2·806	2·25
19	1·336	92·77	10·31	304·35	11·27	2·962	2·37
20	1·406	97·65	10·85	320·37	11·87	3·118	2·49
21	1·476	102·53	11·39	336·39	12·46	3·274	2·62
22	1·547	107·41	11·93	352·40	13·05	3·430	2·74
23	1·617	112·30	12·48	368·42	13·65	3·586	2·87
24	1·687	117·18	13·02	384·44	14·24	3·742	2·99
25	1·758	122·06	13·56	400·46	14·83	3·897	3·12
26	1·828	126·94	14·10	416·48	15·43	4·053	3·24
27	1·898	131·83	14·65	432·50	16·02	4·209	3·37
28	1·969	136·71	15·19	448·51	16·61	4·365	3·49
29	2·039	141·59	15·73	464·53	17·20	4·521	3·62
30	2·109	146·47	16·27	480·55	17·80	4·677	3·74

EQUIVALENTS.

l. ft. ⅌ lb. (Lineal Feet per Pound) = Lineal Metres per Kilogram.
l. yds. ⅌ lb. (Lineal Yards „) = „ „ „
sq. in. ⅌ lb. (Square Inches per Pound) = Sq. Centimetres per Kilogram.
sq. ft. ⅌ lb. („ Feet „) = Square Metres „
sq. yds. ⅌ lb.(„ Yards „) = „ „ „
c. ft. ⅌ ton (Cube Feet per Ton) = Steres(cub.metres) per Tonne.
mls. ⅌ gall. (Miles per Gallon) = Kilometres per Litre.

No.	l. ft. ⅌ lb. =m. ⅌ kg.	l. yds. ⅌ lb. =m. ⅌ kg.	sq. in. ⅌ lb. =sq. cm. ⅌ kg.	sq. ft. ⅌ lb. =sq. m. ⅌ k.	sq. yds. ⅌ lb. =sq. m. ⅌ k.	c. ft. ⅌ ton =stere ⅌ tn.	mls. ⅌ gall =km. ⅌ lit
¼	0·17 m.	0·50 m.	3·56 sq.cm	0·05 sq.m	0·46 sq.m	0·007 st.	0·09 km.
½	0·34	1·01	7·11	0·10	0·92	0·014	0·18
¾	0·50	1·51	10·67	0·15	1·38	0·021	0·27
1	0·67	2·02	14·22	0·20	1·84	0·028	0·35
2	1·34	4·03	28·45	0·41	3·69	0·056	0·71
3	2·02	6·05	42·67	0·61	5·53	0·083	1·06
4	2·69	8·06	56·89	0·82	7·37	0·111	1·42
5	3·36	10·08	71·12	1·02	9·22	0·139	1·77
6	4·03	12·10	85·34	1·23	11·06	0·167	2·12
7	4·70	14·11	99·56	1·43	12·90	0·195	2·48
8	5·38	16·13	113·79	1·64	14·75	0·222	2·83
9	6·05	18·14	128·01	1·84	16·59	0·250	3·19
10	6·72	20·16	142·23	2·05	18·43	0·278	3·54
11	7·39	22·17	156·46	2·25	20·28	0·306	3·89
12	8·06	24·19	170·68	2·46	22·12	0·333	4·25
13	8·74	26·21	184·90	2·66	23·96	0·361	4·60
14	9·41	28·22	199·13	2·87	25·81	0·389	4·96
15	10·08	30·24	213·35	3·07	27·65	0·417	5·31
16	10·75	32·25	227·57	3·28	29·49	0·445	5·66
17	11·42	34·27	241·80	3·48	31·34	0·472	6·02
18	12·10	36·29	256·02	3·69	33·18	0·500	6·37
19	12·77	38·30	270·24	3·89	35·02	0·528	6·73
20	13·44	40·32	284·47	4·10	36·87	0·556	7·08
21	14·11	42·33	298·69	4·30	38·71	0·584	7·43
22	14·78	44·35	312·91	4·51	40·55	0·611	7·79
23	15·46	46·37	327·14	4·71	42·40	0·639	8·14
24	16·13	48·38	341·36	4·92	44·24	0·667	8·50
25	16·80	50·40	355·58	5·12	46·08	0·695	8·85
26	17·47	52·41	369·80	5·33	47·93	0·722	9·20
27	18·14	54·43	384·03	5·53	49·77	0·750	9·56
28	18·81	56·45	398·25	5·73	51·61	0·778	9·91
29	19·49	58·46	412·47	5·94	53·46	0·806	10·27
30	20·16	60·48	426·70	6·14	55·30	0·834	10·62

Brit. H.P.	(British Horse-power)	= Metric Horsepower.
kilowatts	(Kilowatts)	= ,, ,,
miles ϼ gall.	(Miles per Gallon)	= Kilometres per Litre.
tn.-mls. ϼ gall.	(Ton-miles per Gallon)	=Tonne-kilometres ,,
galls. ϼ mile	(Gallons per Mile)	=Litres per Kilometre.
galls. ϼ tn.-ml.	(Gallons per Ton-mile)=Litres per Tonne-kilometre.	
B. Th. U.	(British Thermal Units)=Kilogram-calories.	

No.	Brit. H.P. =met. H.P.	kilowatts =met.H.P.	mls. ▼gall. =km.▼lit.	tn.-ml.▼gal. =tn-km.	gal. ▼ mile =lit. ▼ km.	gal.▼ tn-m. =l.▼tn-km.	B. Th. U. =kg-cal.
¼	0·253mhp	0·34m.	0·09km.	0·09t.m.	0·71lit.	0·70lit.	0·063k.
½	0 ·507	0 ·68	0·18	0·18	1 ·41	1 ·39	0 ·126
¾	0 ·760	1 ·02	0 ·27	0 ·27	2 ·12	2 ·09	0 ·189
1	1 ·014	1 ·36	0 ·35	0 ·36	2 ·82	2 ·78	0 ·252
2	2 ·028	2 ·72	0 ·71	0 ·72	5 ·65	5 ·56	0 ·504
3	3 ·042	4 ·08	1 ·06	1 ·08	8 ·47	8 ·34	0 ·756
4	4 ·055	5 ·44	1 ·42	1 ·44	11 ·30	11 ·12	1 ·008
5	5 ·069	6 ·80	1 ·77	1 ·80	14 ·12	13 ·90	1 ·260
6	6 ·083	8 ·15	2 ·12	2 ·16	16 ·95	16 ·68	1 ·512
7	7 ·097	9 ·51	2 ·48	2 ·52	19 ·77	19 ·46	1 ·764
8	8 ·111	10 ·87	2 ·83	2 ·88	22 ·60	22 ·24	2 ·016
9	9 ·125	12 ·23	3 ·19	3 ·24	25 ·42	25 ·02	2 ·268
10	10 ·139	13 ·59	3 ·54	3 ·60	28 ·25	27 ·80	2 ·520
11	11 ·153	14 ·95	3 ·89	3 ·96	31 ·07	30 ·58	2 ·772
12	12 ·166	16 ·31	4 ·25	4 ·32	33 ·90	33 ·36	3 ·024
13	13 ·180	17 ·67	4 ·60	4 ·68	36 ·72	36 ·14	3 ·276
14	14 ·194	19 ·03	4 ·96	5 ·04	39 ·55	38 ·92	3 ·528
15	15 ·208	20 ·39	5 ·31	5 ·40	42 ·37	41 ·70	3 ·780
16	16 ·222	21 ·75	5 ·66	5 ·75	45 ·20	44 ·48	4 ·032
17	17 ·236	23 ·10	6 ·02	6 ·11	48 ·02	47 ·26	4 ·284
18	18 ·250	24 ·46	6 ·37	6 ·47	50 ·85	50 ·04	4 ·536
19	19 ·263	25 ·82	6 ·73	6 ·83	53 ·67	52 ·82	4 ·788
20	20 ·277	27 ·18	7 ·08	7 ·19	56 ·50	55 ·60	5 ·040
21	21 ·291	28 ·54	7 ·43	7 ·55	59 ·32	58 ·38	5 ·292
22	22 ·305	29 ·90	7 ·79	7 ·91	62 ·15	61 ·16	5 ·544
23	23 ·319	31 ·26	8 ·14	8 ·27	64 ·97	63 ·94	5 ·796
24	24 ·333	32 ·62	8 ·50	8 ·63	67 ·80	66 ·72	6 ·048
25	25 ·347	33 ·98	8 ·85	8 ·99	70 ·62	69 ·50	6 ·300
26	26 ·361	35 ·34	9 ·20	9 ·35	73 ·44	72 ·28	6 ·552
27	27 ·374	36 ·70	9 ·56	9 ·71	76 ·27	75 ·06	6 ·804
28	28 ·388	38 ·05	9 ·91	10 ·07	79 ·09	77 ·84	7 ·056
29	29 ·402	39 ·41	10 ·27	10 ·43	81 ·92	80 ·62	7 ·308
30	30 ·416	40 ·77	10 ·62	10 ·79	84 ·74	83 ·40	7 ·560

° FAHRENHEIT = ° CENTIGRADE.

Fah.	Cent.
0°	*17¾*
2	*16¾*
4	*15½*
6	*14½*
8	*13¼*
10	*12¼*
12	*11*
14	*10*
16	*9*
18	*7¾*
20	*6¾*
22	*5½*
24	*4½*
26	*3¼*
28	*2¼*
30	*1*
31	*−0½*
32°	0°
33	+0½
34	1
35	1¾
36	2¼
37	2¾
38	3¼
39	4
40	4½
41	5
42	5½
43	6
44	6¾
45	7¼
46	7¾
47	8¼
48	9
49	9½
50	10°

Equiv.

Fahr.	Cent.
1°	=0½
2	1
3	1¾
4	2¼
5	2¾
6	3¼
7	4
8	4½
9	5

Fahr.	Cent.	Fahr.	Cent.	Fahr.	Cent.	Fahr.	Cent.	Fahr.	Cent.
51	10½	91	32¾	142	61	220	104	572	300
52	11	92	33¼	144	62¼	230	110	600	316
53	11¾	93	34	146	63¼	240	116	700	371
54	12¼	94	34½	148	64½	248	120	752	400
55	12¾	95	35	149	65	**250**	121	800	427
56	13¼	96	35½	**150**	65½	260	127	900	482
57	14	97	36	152	66¾	266	130	932	500
58	14½	98	36¾	154	67¾	270	132	1000	538
59	15	99	37¼	156	69	280	138	1100	593
60	15½	**100**	37¾	158	70	284	140	1112	600
61	16	101	38¼	**160**	71	290	143	1200	649
62	16¾	102	39	162	72¼	**300**	149	1292	700
63	17¼	103	39½	164	73¼	302	150	1300	704
64	17¾	104	40	166	74½	310	154	1400	760
65	18¼	105	40½	167	75	320	160	1472	800
66	19	106	41	168	75½	330	166	1500	816
67	19½	107	41¾	**170**	76¾	338	170	1600	871
68	20	108	42¼	172	77¾	340	171	1652	900
69	20½	109	42¾	174	79	**350**	177	1700	927
70	21	**110**	43¼	176	80	356	180	1800	982
71	21¾	111	44	178	81	360	182	1832	1000
72	22¼	112	44½	**180**	82¼	370	188	1900	1038
73	22¾	113	45	182	83¼	374	190	2000	1093
74	23¼	114	45½	184	84½	380	193	2012	1100
75	24	115	46	185	85	390	199	2100	1149
76	24½	116	46¾	186	85½	392	200	2192	1200
77	25	117	47¼	188	86¾	**400**	204	2200	1204
78	25½	118	47¾	**190**	87¾	410	210	2300	1260
79	26	119	48¼	192	89	420	216	2372	1300
80	26¾	**120**	49	194	90	430	221	2400	1316
81	27¼	122	50	196	91	440	227	2500	1371
82	27¾	124	51	198	92¼	446	230	2552	1400
83	28¼	126	52¼	**200**	93¼	**450**	232	2600	1427
84	29	128	53¼	202	94½	460	238	2700	1482
85	29½	**130**	54½	203	95	464	240	2732	1500
86	30	132	55½	204	95½	470	243	2800	1538
87	30½	134	56¾	206	96¾	480	249	2900	1593
88	31	136	57¾	208	97¾	482	250	2912	1600
89	31¾	138	59	210	99	490	254	3000	1649
90	32¼	**140**	60	**212**	100	**500**	260	3100	1704

I.

BRITISH LINEAL MEASURES

CONVERTED INTO METRIC.

Contractions[2].

Contraction[3].		Plural[3]=	Contraction[3].		Plural[3]=
cm.	=centimetre;	(centimetres)	m., met.	=metre ;	(metres)
ft. ...	=foot ;	(feet)	ml., mls.	=mile ;	(miles)
fur. ...	=furlong ;	(furlongs)	mm.	=millimetre ;	(millimetres)
in., ins.	=inch ;	(inches)	po. ...	=pole ;	(poles)
km.	=kilometre ;	(kilometres)	yd., yds.	=yard ;	(yards)

I.

MESURES ANGLAISES DE LONGUEURS converties en mesures metriques.

ENGLISCHE LANGENMASSE zu metrischen umgerechnet.

MISURE INGLESI DI LUNGHESSE convertite in misure metriche.

MEDIDAS LINEALES INGLESAS convertidas al sistema metrico.

Français.	Deutsch.	Italiano.	Español.
[1] Pages.	[1] Zeiten.	[1] Pagini.	[1] Paginas.
[2] Contraction.	[2] Abkürzungen.	[2] Contrazione.	[2] Contracciones.
[3] Pluriel.	[3] Mehrzahl.	[3] Plurale.	[3] Plural.

INCHES — MILLIMETRES.

Ins.	=mm.	Ins.	=mm.	Ins.	=mm.	Ins.	=mm.
1/64	0·3969	41/64	16·2719	2 1/16	52·3875	4 9/16	115·8875
1/32	0·7937	21/32	16·6687	1/8	53·9750	5/8	117·4750
3/64	1·1906	43/64	17·0656	3/16	55·5625	11/16	119·0625
1/16	1·5875	11/16	17·4625	2 1/4	57·1500	4 3/4	120·6500
5/64	1·9844	45/64	17·8594	5/16	58·7375	13/16	122·2375
3/32	2·3812	23/32	18·2562	3/8	60·3250	7/8	123·8250
7/64	2·7781	47/64	18·6531	7/16	61·9125	15/16	125·4125
1/8"	3·1750	3/4"	19·0500	2 1/2	63·5000	5"	127·0000
9/64	3·5719	49/64	19·4469	9/16	65·0875	1/16	128·5875
5/32	3·9687	25/32	19·8437	5/8	66·6750	1/8	130·1750
11/64	4·3656	51/64	20·2406	11/16	68·2625	3/16	131·7625
3/16	4·7625	13/16	20·6375	2 3/4	69·8500	5 1/4	133·3500
13/64	5·1594	53/64	21·0344	13/16	71·4375	5/16	134·9375
7/32	5·5562	27/32	21·4312	7/8	73·0250	3/8	136·5250
15/64	5·9531	55/64	21·8281	15/16	74·6125	7/16	138·1125
1/4"	6·3500	7/8"	22·2250	3"	76·2000	5 1/2	139·7000
17/64	6·7469	57/64	22·6219	1/16	77·7875	9/16	141·2875
9/32	7·1437	29/32	23·0187	1/8	79·3750	5/8	142·8750
19/64	7·5406	59/64	23·4156	3/16	80·9625	11/16	144·4625
5/16	7·9375	15/16	23·8125	3 1/4	82·5500	5 3/4	146·0500
21/64	8·3344	61/64	24·2094	5/16	84·1375	13/16	147·6375
11/32	8·7312	31/32	24·6062	3/8	85·7250	7/8	149·2250
23/64	9·1281	63/64	25·0031	7/16	87·3125	15/16	150·8125
3/8"	9·5250	1"	25·4000	3 1/2	88·9000	6"	152·4000
25/64	9·9219	1/16	26·9875	9/16	90·4875	1/16	153·9875
13/32	10·3187	1/8	28·5750	5/8	92·0750	1/8	155·5750
27/64	10·7156	3/16	30·1625	11/16	93·6625	3/16	157·1625
7/16	11·1125	1 1/4	31·7500	3 3/4	95·2500	6 1/4	158·7500
29/64	11·5094	5/16	33·3375	13/16	96·8375	5/16	160·3375
15/32	11·9062	3/8	34·9250	7/8	98·4250	3/8	161·9250
31/64	12·3031	7/16	36·5125	15/16	100·0125	7/16	163·5125
1/2"	12·7000	1 1/2	38·1000	4"	101·6000	6 1/2	165·1000
33/64	13·0969	9/16	39·6875	1/16	103·1875	9/16	166·6875
17/32	13·4937	5/8	41·2750	1/8	104·7750	5/8	168·2750
35/64	13·8906	11/16	42·8625	3/16	106·3625	11/16	169·8625
9/16	14·2875	1 3/4	44·4500	4 1/4	107·9500	6 3/4	171·4500
37/64	14·6844	13/16	46·0375	5/16	109·5375	13/16	173·0375
19/32	15·0812	7/8	47·6250	3/8	111·1250	7/8	174·6250
39/64	15·4781	15/16	49·2125	7/16	112·7125	15/16	176·2125
5/8"	15·8750	2"	50·8000	4 1/2	114·3000	7"	177·8000

Ins.	=mm.	Ins.	=mm.	ins.	Ft. ins.	=mm.
7 1/16	179·3875	9 9/16	242·8875	12 1/8	1.0 1/8	307·9750
1/8	180·9750	5/8	244·4750	12 1/4	0 1/4	311·1500
3/16	182·5625	11/16	246·0625	12 3/8	0 3/8	314·3250
7 1/4	184·1500	9 3/4	247·6500	12 1/2	1.0 1/2	317·5000
5/16	185·7375	13/16	249·2375	12 5/8	0 5/8	320·6750
3/8	187·3250	7/8	250·8250	12 3/4	0 3/4	323·8500
7/16	188·9125	15/16	252·4125	12 7/8	0 7/8	327·0250
7 1/2	190·5000	10"	254·0000	13	1.1	330·2000
9/16	192·0875	1/16	255·5875	13 1/8	1.1 1/8	333·3750
5/8	193·6750	1/8	257·1750	13 1/4	1 1/4	336·5500
11/16	195·2625	3/16	258·7625	13 3/8	1 3/8	339·7250
7 3/4	196·8500	10 1/4	260·3500	13 1/2	1.1 1/2	342·9000
13/16	198·4375	5/16	261·9375	13 5/8	1 5/8	346·0750
7/8	200·0250	3/8	263·5250	13 3/4	1 3/4	349·2500
15/16	201·6125	7/16	265·1125	13 7/8	1 7/8	352·4250
8"	203·2000	10 1/2	266·7000	14	1.2	355·6000
1/16	204·7875	9/16	268·2875	14 1/8	2 1/8	358·7750
1/8	206·3750	5/8	269·8750	14 1/4	2 1/4	361·9500
3/16	207·9625	11/16	271·4625	14 3/8	2 3/8	365·1250
8 1/4	209·5500	10 3/4	273·0500	14 1/2	1.2 1/2	368·3000
5/16	211·1375	13/16	274·6375	14 5/8	2 5/8	371·4750
3/8	212·7250	7/8	276·2250	14 3/4	2 3/4	374·6500
7/16	214·3125	15/16	277·8125	14 7/8	2 7/8	377·8250
8 1/2	215·9000	11"	279·4000	15	1.3	381·0000
9/16	217·4875	1/16	280·9875	15 1/4	3 1/4	387·3500
5/8	219·0750	1/8	282·5750	15 1/2	3 1/2	393·7000
11/16	220·6625	3/16	284·1625	15 3/4	3 3/4	400·0500
8 3/4	222·2500	11 1/4	285·7500	16	1.4	406·4000
13/16	223·8375	5/16	287·3375	16 1/4	4 1/4	412·7500
7/8	225·4250	3/8	288·9250	16 1/2	4 1/2	419·1000
15/16	227·0125	7/16	290·5125	16 3/4	4 3/4	425·4500
9"	228·6000	11 1/2	292·1000	17	1.5	431·8000
1/16	230·1875	9/16	293·6875	17 1/4	5 1/4	438·1500
1/8	231·7750	5/8	295·2750	17 1/2	5 1/2	444·5000
3/16	233·3625	11/16	296·8625	17 3/4	5 3/4	450·8500
9 1/4	234·9500	11 3/4	298·4500	18	1.6	457·2000
5/16	236·5375	13/16	300·0375	24	2 feet	609·6000
3/8	238·1250	7/8	301·6250	36	3 ft.	914·4000
7/16	239·7125	15/16	303·2125	48	4 ft.	1219·2000
9 1/2"	241·3000	12"	304·8000	60	5 feet	1524·0000

4. FEET & INCHES — METRES & MILLIMETRES.

ins.	Ft.ins.	met. mm.	ins.	Ft.ins.	met. mm.	ins.	Ft.ins.	met. mm.
18¼	1.6¼	0 463·55	27¼	2.3¼	0 692·15	36¼	3.0¼	0 920·75
18½	½	0 469·90	27½	½	0 698·50	36½	½	0 927·10
18¾	¾	0 476·25	27¾	¾	0 704·85	36¾	¾	0 933·45
19	1.7	0 482·60	28	2.4	0 711·20	37	3.1	0 939·80
19¼	¼	0 488·95	28¼	¼	0 717·55	37¼	¼	0 946·15
19½	½	0 495·30	28½	½	0 723·90	37½	½	0 952·50
19¾	¾	0 501·65	28¾	¾	0 730·25	37¾	¾	0 958·85
20	1.8	0 508·00	29	2.5	0 736·60	38	3.2	0 965·20
20¼	¼	0 514·35	29¼	¼	0 742·95	38¼	¼	0 971·55
20½	½	0 520·70	29½	½	0 749·30	38½	½	0 977·90
20¾	¾	0 527·05	29¾	¾	0 755·65	38¾	¾	0 984·25
21	1.9	0 533·40	30	2.6	0 762·00	39	3.3	0 990·60
21¼	¼	0 539·75	30¼	¼	0 768·35	39¼	¼	0 996·95
21½	½	0 546·10	30½	½	0 774·70	39½	½	1 003·30
21¾	¾	0 552·45	30¾	¾	0 781·05	39¾	¾	1 009·65
22	1.10	0 558·80	31	2.7	0 787·40	40	3.4	1 016·00
22¼	¼	0 565·15	31¼	¼	0 793·75	40¼	¼	1 022·35
22½	½	0 571·50	31½	½	0 800·10	40½	½	1 028·70
22¾	¾	0 577·85	31¾	¾	0 806·45	40¾	¾	1 035·05
23	1.11	0 584·20	32	2.8	0 812·80	41	3.5	1 041·40
23¼	¼	0 590·55	32¼	¼	0 819·15	41¼	¼	1 047·75
23½	½	0 596·90	32½	½	0 825·50	41½	½	1 054·10
23¾	¾	0 603·25	32¾	¾	0 831·85	41¾	¾	1 060·45
24	2. 0	0 609·60	33	2.9	0 838·20	42	3.6	1 066·80
24¼	¼	0 615·95	33¼	¼	0 844·55	42¼	¼	1 073·15
24½	½	0 622·30	33½	½	0 850·90	42½	½	1 079·50
24¾	¾	0 628·65	33¾	¾	0 857·25	42¾	¾	1 085·85
25	2.1	0 635·00	34	2.10	0 863·60	43	3.7	1 092·20
25¼	¼	0 641·35	34¼	¼	0 869·95	43¼	¼	1 098·55
25½	½	0 647·70	34½	½	0 876·30	43½	½	1 104·90
25¾	¾	0 654·05	34¾	¾	0 882·65	43¾	¾	1 111·25
26	2.2	0 660·40	35	2.11	0 889·00	44	3.8	1 117·60
26¼	¼	0 666·75	35¼	¼	0 895·35	44¼	¼	1 123·95
26½	½	0 673·10	35½	½	0 901·70	44½	½	1 130·30
26¾	¾	0 679·45	35¾	¾	0 908·05	44¾	¾	1 136·65
27	2. 3	0 685·80	36	3.0	0 914·40	45	3. 9	1 143·00

ins.	Feet	met. mm.	ins.	Feet	met. mm.	ins.	Feet	met. mm.
360	30	9 144·0	840	70	21 336·0	1320	110	33 528·0
480	40	12 192·0	960	80	24 384·0	1440	120	36 576·0
600	50	15 240·0	1080	90	27 432·0	1560	130	39 624·0
720	60	18 288·0	1200	100	30 480·0	1680	140	42 672·0

ins.	Ft.ins.	met.	mm.	ins.	Ft.ins.	met.	mm.	ins.	Ft.ins.	met.	mm.
45¼	3.9¼	1	149·35	54¼	4.6¼	1	377·95	63¼	5.3¼	1	606·55
45½	½	1	155·70	54½	½	1	384·30	63½	½	1	612·90
45¾	¾	1	162·05	54¾	¾	1	390·65	63¾	¾	1	619·25
46	3.10	1	168·40	55	4.7	1	397·00	64	5.4	1	625·60
46¼	¼	1	174·75	55¼	¼	1	403·35	64¼	¼	1	631·95
46½	½	1	181·10	55½	½	1	409·70	64½	½	1	638·30
46¾	¾	1	187·45	55¾	¾	1	416·05	64¾	¾	1	644·65
47	3.11	1	193·80	56	4.8	1	422·40	65	5.5	1	651·00
47¼	¼	1	200·15	56¼	¼	1	428·75	65¼	¼	1	657·35
47½	½	1	206·50	56½	½	1	435·10	65½	½	1	663·70
47¾	¾	1	212·85	56¾	¾	1	441·45	65¾	¾	1	670·05
48	4.0	1	219·20	57	4.9	1	447·80	66	5.6	1	676·40
48¼	¼	1	225·55	57¼	¼	1	454·15	66¼	¼	1	682·75
48½	½	1	231·90	57½	½	1	460·50	66½	½	1	689·10
48¾	¾	1	238·25	57¾	¾	1	466·85	66¾	¾	1	695·45
49	4.1	1	244·60	58	4.10	1	473·20	67	5.7	1	701·80
49¼	¼	1	250·95	58¼	¼	1	479·55	67¼	¼	1	708·15
49½	½	1	257·30	58½	½	1	485·90	67½	½	1	714·50
49¾	¾	1	263·65	58¾	¾	1	492·25	67¾	¾	1	720·85
50	4.2	1	270·00	59	4.11	1	498·60	68	5.8	1	727·20
50¼	¼	1	276·35	59¼	¼	1	504·95	68¼	¼	1	733·55
50½	½	1	282·70	59½	½	1	511·30	68½	½	1	739·90
50¾	¾	1	289·05	59¾	¾	1	517·65	68¾	¾	1	746·25
51	4.3	1	295·40	60	5.0	1	524·00	69	5.9	1	752·60
51¼	¼	1	301·75	60¼	¼	1	530·35	69¼	¼	1	758·95
51½	½	1	308·10	60½	½	1	536·70	69½	½	1	765·30
51¾	¾	1	314·45	60¾	¾	1	543·05	69¾	¾	1	771·65
52	4.4	1	320·80	61	5.1	1	549·40	70	5.10	1	778·00
52¼	¼	1	327·15	61¼	¼	1	555·75	70¼	¼	1	784·35
52½	½	1	333·50	61½	½	1	562·10	70½	½	1	790·70
52¾	¾	1	339·85	61¾	¾	1	568·45	70¾	¾	1	797·05
53	4.5	1	346·20	62	5.2	1	574·80	71	5.11	1	803·40
53¼	¼	1	352·55	62¼	¼	1	581·15	71¼	¼	1	809·75
53½	½	1	358·90	62½	½	1	587·50	71½	½	1	816·10
53¾	¾	1	365·25	62¾	¾	1	593·85	71¾	¾	1	822·45
54	4.6	1	371·60	63	5.3	1	600·20	72	6.0	1	828·80

ins.	Ft.ins.	met.	mm.	ins.	Ft.ins.	met.	mm.	ins.	Ft.ins.	met.	mm.
72½	6.0½	1	841·5	74½	6.2½	1	892·3	76½	6.4½	1	943·1
73	1	1	854·2	75	3	1	905·0	77	5	1	955·8
73½	1½	1	866·9	75½	3½	1	917·7	77½	5½	1	968·5
74	6.2	1	879·6	76	6.4	1	930·4	78	6.6	1	981·2

6.   FEET & INCHES — METRES & MILLIMETRES.

ins.	Ft. ins.	met. mm.	ins.	Ft. ins.	met. mm.	ins.	Ft. ins.	met. mm.
73	6.1	1 854·2	109	9.1	2 768·6	145	12.1	3 683·0
74	2	1 879·6	110	2	2 794·0	146	2	3 708·4
75	3	1 905·0	111	3	2 819·4	147	3	3 733·8
76	4	1 930·4	112	4	2 844·8	148	4	3 759·2
77	5	1 955·8	113	5	2 870·2	149	5	3 784·6
78	6	1 981·2	114	6	2 895·6	150	6	3 810·0
79	7	2 006·6	115	7	2 921·0	151	7	3 835·4
80	8	2 032·0	116	8	2 946·4	152	8	3 860·8
81	9	2 057·4	117	9	2 971·8	153	9	3 886·2
82	10	2 082·8	118	10	2 997·2	154	10	3 911·6
83	11	2 108·2	119	11	3 022·6	155	11	3 937·0
84	7 ft.	2 133·6	120	10 ft.	3 048·0	156	13 ft.	3 962·4
85	1	2 159·0	121	1	3 073·4	157	1	3 987·8
86	2	2 184·4	122	2	3 098·8	158	2	4 013·2
87	3	2 209·8	123	3	3 124·2	159	3	4 038·6
88	4	2 235·2	124	4	3 149·6	160	4	4 064·0
89	5	2 260·6	125	5	3 175·0	161	5	4 089·4
90	6	2 286·0	126	6	3 200·4	162	6	4 114·8
91	7	2 311·4	127	7	3 225·8	163	7	4 140·2
92	8	2 336·8	128	8	3 251·2	164	8	4 165·6
93	9	2 362·2	129	9	3 276·6	165	9	4 191·0
94	10	2 387·6	130	10	3 302·0	166	10	4 216·4
95	11	2 413·0	131	11	3 327·4	167	11	4 241·8
96	8 ft.	2 438·4	132	11 ft.	3 352·8	168	14 ft.	4 267·2
97	1	2 463·8	133	1	3 378·2	169	1	4 292·6
98	2	2 489·2	134	2	3 403·6	170	2	4 318·0
99	3	2 514·6	135	3	3 429·0	171	3	4 343·4
100	4	2 540·0	136	4	3 454·4	172	4	4 368·8
101	5	2 565·4	137	5	3 479·8	173	5	4 394·2
102	6	2 590·8	138	6	3 505·2	174	6	4 419·6
103	7	2 616·2	139	7	3 530·6	175	7	4 445·0
104	8	2 641·6	140	8	3 556·0	176	8	4 470·4
105	9	2 667·0	141	9	3 581·4	177	9	4 495·8
106	10	2 692·4	142	10	3 606·8	178	10	4 521·2
107	11	2 717·8	143	11	3 632·2	189	11	4 546·6
108	9 ft.	2 743·2	144	12 ft.	3 657·6	180	15 ft.	4 572·0

ins.	Feet	met. mm.	ins.	Feet	met. mm.	ins.	Feet	met. mm.
360	30	9 144·0	840	70	21 336·0	1320	110	33 528·0
480	40	12 192·0	960	80	24 384·0	1440	120	36 576·0
600	50	15 240·0	1080	90	27 432·0	1560	130	39 624·0
720	60	18 288·0	1200	100	30 480·0	1680	140	42 672·0

ins.	Ft. ins.	met.	mm.	ins.	Ft. ins.	met.	mm.	ins.	Ft. ins.	met.	mm.
181	15.1	4	597·4	217	18.1	5	511·8	253	21.1	6	426·2
182	2	4	622·8	218	2	5	537·2	254	2	6	451·6
183	3	4	648·2	219	3	5	562·6	255	3	6	477·0
184	4	4	673·6	220	4	5	588·0	256	4	6	502·4
185	5	4	699·0	221	5	5	613·4	257	5	6	527·8
186	6	4	724·4	222	6	5	638·8	258	6	6	553·2
187	7	4	749·8	223	7	5	664·2	259	7	6	578·6
188	8	4	775·2	224	8	5	689·6	260	8	6	604·0
189	9	4	800·6	225	9	5	715·0	261	9	6	629·4
190	10	4	826·0	226	10	5	740·4	262	10	6	654·8
191	11	4	851·4	227	11	5	765·8	263	11	6	680·2
192	16 ft.	4	876·8	228	19 ft.	5	791·2	264	22 ft.	6	705·6
193	1	4	902·2	229	1	5	816·6	265	1	6	731·0
194	2	4	927·6	230	2	5	842·0	266	2	6	756·4
195	3	4	953·0	231	3	5	867·4	267	3	6	781·8
196	4	4	978·4	232	4	5	892·8	268	4	6	807·2
197	5	5	003·8	233	5	5	918·2	269	5	6	832·6
198	6	5	029·2	234	6	5	943·6	270	6	6	858·0
199	7	5	054·6	235	7	5	969·0	271	7	6	883·4
200	8	5	080·0	236	8	5	994·4	272	8	6	908·8
201	9	5	105·4	237	9	6	019·8	273	9	6	934·2
202	10	5	130·8	238	10	6	045·2	274	10	6	959·6
203	11	5	156·2	239	11	6	070·6	275	11	6	985·0
204	17 ft.	5	181·6	240	20 ft.	6	096·0	276	23 ft.	7	010·4
205	1	5	207·0	241	1	6	121·4	277	1	7	035·8
206	2	5	232·4	242	2	6	146·8	278	2	7	061·2
207	3	5	257·8	243	3	6	172·2	279	3	7	086·6
208	4	5	283·2	244	4	6	197·6	280	4	7	112·0
209	5	5	308·6	245	5	6	223·0	281	5	7	137·4
210	6	5	334·0	246	6	6	248·4	282	6	7	162·8
211	7	5	359·4	247	7	6	273·8	283	7	7	188·2
212	8	5	384·8	248	8	6	299·2	284	8	7	213·6
213	9	5	410·2	249	9	6	324·6	285	9	7	239·0
214	10	5	435·6	250	10	6	350·0	286	10	7	264·4
215	11	5	461·0	251	11	6	375·4	287	11	7	289·8
216	18 ft.	5	486·4	252	21 ft.	6	400·8	288	24 ft.	7	315·2
289	24.1	7	340·6	293	24.5	7	442·2	297	24.9	7	543·8
290	2	7	366·0	294	6	7	467·6	298	10	7	569·2
291	3	7	391·4	295	7	7	493·0	299	11	7	594·6
292	24.4	7	416·8	296	24.8	7	518·4	300	25 ft.	7	620·0

YARDS & FEET — METRES.

yds.	metres	mm.	feet	yds.	metres	mm.	feet	yds.	metres	mm.	feet
...	0	305	1	...	9	449	31	...	18	593	61
...	0	610	2	...	9	754	32	...	18	898	62
1	0	914	3	11	10	058	33	21	19	202	63
...	1	219	4	...	10	363	34	...	19	507	64
...	1	524	5	...	10	668	35	...	19	812	65
2	1	829	6	12	10	973	36	22	20	117	66
...	2	134	7	...	11	278	37	...	20	422	67
...	2	438	8	...	11	582	38	...	20	726	68
3	2	743	9	13	11	887	39	23	21	031	69
...	3	048	10	...	12	192	40	...	21	336	70
...	3	353	11	...	12	497	41	...	21	641	71
4	3	658	12	14	12	802	42	24	21	946	72
...	3	962	13	...	13	106	43	...	22	250	73
...	4	267	14	...	13	411	44	...	22	555	74
5	4	572	15	15	13	716	45	25	22	860	75
...	4	877	16	...	14	021	46	...	23	165	76
...	5	182	17	...	14	326	47	...	23	470	77
6	5	486	18	16	14	630	48	26	23	774	78
...	5	791	19	...	14	935	49	...	24	079	79
...	6	096	20	...	15	240	50	...	24	384	80
7	6	401	21	17	15	545	51	27	24	689	81
...	6	706	22	...	15	850	52	...	24	994	82
...	7	010	23	...	16	154	53	...	25	298	83
8	7	315	24	18	16	459	54	28	25	603	84
...	7	620	25	...	16	764	55	...	25	908	85
...	7	925	26	...	17	069	56	...	26	213	86
9	8	230	27	19	17	374	57	29	26	518	87
...	8	534	28	...	17	678	58	...	26	822	88
...	8	839	29	...	17	983	59	...	27	127	89
10	9	144	30	20	18	288	60	30	27	432	90

Ins	=mm.	Yds.	=mm	yds.	metres mm.	feet	yds.	metres mm.	feet
1	25·4	1/16	57	100	91 440	300	1100	1005 839	3300
2	50·8	1/8	114	200	182 880	600	1200	1097 279	3600
3	76·2			300	274 320	900	1300	1188 719	3900
4	101·6	1/4...	229	400	365 760	1200	1400	1280 159	4200
5	127·0	3/8	343	500	457 200	1500	1500	1371 599	4500
6	152·4			600	548 639	1800	1600	1463 038	4800
7	177·8	1/2...	457	700	640 079	2100	1700	1554 478	5100
8	203·2	5/8	572	800	731 519	2400	1800	1645 918	5400
9	228·6	3/4...	686	900	822 959	2700	1900	1737 358	5700
10	254·0			1000	914 399	3000	2000	1828 798	6000
11	279·4	7/8	800						

yds.	metres mm.	feet	yds.	metres mm.	feet	yds.	metres mm.	feet
...	27 737	91	...	36 881	121	...	46 025	151
...	28 042	92	...	37 186	122	...	46 330	152
31	28 346	93	41	37 490	123	51	46 634	153
...	28 651	94	...	37 795	124	...	46 939	154
...	28 956	95	...	38 100	125	...	47 244	155
32	29 261	96	42	38 405	126	52	47 549	156
...	29 566	97	...	38 710	127	...	47 854	157
...	29 870	98	...	39 014	128	...	48 158	158
33	30 175	99	43	39 319	129	53	48 463	159
...	30 480	100	...	39 624	130	...	48 768	160
...	30 785	101	...	39 929	131	...	49 073	161
34	31 090	102	44	40 234	132	54	49 378	162
...	31 394	103	...	40 538	133	...	49 682	163
...	31 699	104	...	40 843	134	...	49 987	164
35	32 004	105	45	41 148	135	55	50 292	165
...	32 309	106	...	41 453	136	...	50 597	166
...	32 614	107	...	41 758	137	...	50 902	167
36	32 918	108	46	42 062	138	56	51 206	168
...	33 223	109	...	42 367	139	...	51 511	169
...	33 528	110	...	42 672	140	...	51 816	170
37	33 833	111	47	42 977	141	57	52 121	171
...	34 138	112	...	43 282	142	...	52 426	172
...	34 442	113	...	43 586	143	...	52 730	173
38	34 747	114	48	43 891	144	58	53 035	174
...	35 052	115	...	44 196	145	...	53 340	175
...	35 357	116	...	44 501	146	...	53 645	176
39	35 662	117	49	44 806	147	59	53 950	177
...	35 966	118	...	45 110	148	...	54 254	178
...	36 271	119	...	45 415	149	...	54 559	179
40	36 576	120	50	45 720	150	60	54 864	180

yds.	metres mm.	feet	yds.	metres mm.	feet	yds.	metres mm.	feet
2100	1920 238	6300	3200	2926 077	9600	4800	4389 115	14400
2200	2011 678	6600	3400	3108 957	10200	5000	4571 995	15000
2300	2103 118	6900	3500	3200 397	10500	6000	5486 394	18000
2400	2194 558	7200	3600	3291 836	10800	7000	6400 793	21000
2500	2285 998	7500	3800	3474 716	11400	8000	7315 192	24000
2600	2377 437	7800	4000	3657 596	12000	9000	8229 591	27000
2700	2468 877	8100	4200	3840 476	12600	10000	9143 990	30000
2800	2560 317	8400	4400	4023 356	13200	15000	13715 985	45000
2900	2651 757	8700	4500	4114 796	13500	20000	18287 980	60000
3000	2743 197	9000	4600	4206 235	13800	25000	22859 975	75000

B

yds.	metres mm.	feet	yds.	metres mm.	feet	yds.	metres mm.	feet
...	55 169	181	...	64 313	211	...	73 457	241
...	55 474	182	...	64 618	212	...	73 762	242
61	55 778	183	71	64 922	213	81	74 066	243
...	56 083	184	...	65 227	214	...	74 371	244
...	56 388	185	...	65 532	215	...	74 676	245
62	56 693	186	72	65 837	216	82	74 981	246
...	56 998	187	...	66 142	217	...	75 286	247
...	57 302	188	...	66 446	218	...	75 590	248
63	57 607	189	73	66 751	219	83	75 895	249
...	57 912	190	...	67 056	220	...	76 200	250
...	58 217	191	...	67 361	221	...	76 505	251
64	58 522	192	74	67 666	222	84	76 810	252
...	58 826	193	...	67 970	223	...	77 114	253
...	59 131	194	...	68 275	224	...	77 419	254
65	59 436	195	75	68 580	225	85	77 724	255
...	59 741	196	...	68 885	226	...	78 029	256
...	60 046	197	...	69 190	227	...	78 334	257
66	60 350	198	76	69 494	228	86	78 638	258
...	60 655	199	...	69 799	229	...	78 943	259
...	60 960	200	...	70 104	230	...	79 248	260
67	61 265	201	77	70 409	231	87	79 553	261
...	61 570	202	...	70 714	232	...	79 858	262
...	61 874	203	...	71 018	233	...	80 162	263
68	62 179	204	78	71 323	234	88	80 467	264
...	62 484	205	...	71 628	235	...	80 772	265
...	62 789	206	...	71 933	236	...	81 077	266
69	63 094	207	79	72 238	237	89	81 382	267
...	63 398	208	...	72 542	238	...	81 686	268
...	63 703	209	...	72 847	239	...	81 991	269
70	64 008	210	80	73 152	240	90	82 296	270

Ins	=mm.
1	25·4
2	50·8
3	76·2
4	101·6
5	127·0
6	152·4
7	177·8
8	203·2
9	228·6
10	254·0
11	279·4

Yds.	=mm
1/16	57
1/8	114
1/4	229
3/8	343
1/2	457
5/8	572
3/4	686
7/8	800

yds.	metres mm.	feet	yds.	metres mm.	feet
100	91 440	300	1100	1005 839	3300
200	182 880	600	1200	1097 279	3600
300	274 320	900	1300	1188 719	3900
400	365 760	1200	1400	1280 159	4200
500	457 200	1500	1500	1371 599	4500
600	548 639	1800	1600	1463 038	4800
700	640 079	2100	1700	1554 478	5100
800	731 519	2400	1800	1645 918	5400
900	822 959	2700	1900	1737 358	5700
1000	914 399	3000	2000	1828 798	6000

yds.	metres mm.	feet	yds.	metres mm.	feet	yds.	metres mm.	feet
...	82 601	271	...	91 745	301	...	100 889	331
...	82 906	272	...	92 050	302	...	101 194	332
91	83 210	273	101	92 354	303	111	101 498	333
...	83 515	274	...	92 659	304	...	101 803	334
...	83 820	275	...	92 964	305	...	102 108	335
92	84 125	276	102	93 269	306	112	102 413	336
...	84 430	277	...;	93 574	307	...	102 718	337
...	84 734	278	...	93 878	308	...	103 022	338
93	85 039	279	103	94 183	309	113	103 327	339
...	85 344	280	...	94 488	310	...	103 632	340
...	85 649	281	...	94 793	311	...	103 937	341
94	85 954	282	104	95 098	312	114	104 242	342
...	86 258	283	...	95 402	313	...	104 546	343
...	86 563	284	...	95 707	314	...	104 851	344
95	86 868	285	105	96 012	315	115	105 156	345
...	87 173	286	...	96 317	316	...	105 461	346
...	87 478	287	...	96 622	317	...	105 766	347
96	87 782	288	106	96 926	318	116	106 070	348
...	88 087	289	...	97 231	319	...	106 375	349
...	88 392	290	...	97 536	320	...	106 680	350
97	88 697	291	107	97 841	321	117	106 985	351
...	89 002	292	...	98 146	322	...	107 290	352
...	89 306	293	...	98 450	323	...	107 594	353
98	89 611	294	108	98 755	324	118	107 899	354
...	89 916	295	...	99 060	325	...	108 204	355
...	90 221	296	...	99 365	326	...	108 509	356
99	90 526	297	109	99 670	327	119	108 814	357
...	90 830	298	...	99 974	328	...	109 118	358
...	91 135	299	...	100 279	329	...	109 423	359
100	91 440	300	110	100 584	330	120	109 728	360

yds.	metres mm.	feet	yds.	metres mm.	feet	yds.	metres mm.	feet
2100	1920 238	6300	3200	2926 077	9600	4800	4389 115	14400
2200	2011 678	6600	3400	3108 957	10200	5000	4571 995	15000
2300	2103 118	6900	3500	3200 397	10500	6000	5486 394	18000
2400	2194 558	7200	3600	3291 836	10800	7000	6400 793	21000
2500	2285 998	7500	3800	3474 716	11400	8000	7315 192	24000
2600	2377 437	7800	4000	3657 596	12000	9000	8229 591	27000
2700	2468 877	8100	4200	3840 476	12600	10000	9143 990	30000
2800	2560 317	8400	4400	4023 356	13200	15000	13715 985	45000
2900	2651 757	8700	4500	4114 796	13500	20000	18287 980	60000
3000	2743 197	9000	4600	4206 235	13800	25000	22859 975	75000

YARDS — METRES.

Yds.	metres	mm.	Yds.	metres	mm.	Yds.	metres	mm.	Yds.	metres	mm.
121	110	642	161	147	218	201	183	794	241	220	370
122	111	557	162	148	133	202	184	709	242	221	285
123	112	471	163	149	047	203	185	623	243	222	199
124	113	386	164	149	962	204	186	538	244	223	114
125	114	300	165	150	876	205	187	452	245	224	028
126	115	214	166	151	790	206	188	366	246	224	942
127	116	129	167	152	705	207	189	281	247	225	857
128	117	043	168	153	619	208	190	195	248	226	771
129	117	958	169	154	534	209	191	110	249	227	686
130	118	872	170	155	448	210	192	024	250	228	600
131	119	786	171	156	362	211	192	938	251	229	514
132	120	701	172	157	277	212	193	853	252	230	429
133	121	615	173	158	191	213	194	767	253	231	343
134	122	530	174	159	106	214	195	682	254	232	258
135	123	444	175	160	020	215	196	596	255	233	172
136	124	358	176	160	934	216	197	510	256	234	086
137	125	273	177	161	849	217	198	425	257	235	001
138	126	187	178	162	763	218	199	339	258	235	915
139	127	102	179	163	678	219	200	254	259	236	830
140	128	016	180	164	592	220	201	168	260	237	744
141	128	930	181	165	506	221	202	082	261	238	658
142	129	845	182	166	421	222	202	997	262	239	573
143	130	759	183	167	335	223	203	911	263	240	487
144	131	674	184	168	250	224	204	826	264	241	402
145	132	588	185	169	164	225	205	740	265	242	316
146	133	502	186	170	078	226	206	654	266	243	230
147	134	417	187	170	993	227	207	569	267	244	145
148	135	331	188	171	907	228	208	483	268	245	059
149	136	246	189	172	822	229	209	398	269	245	974
150	137	160	190	173	736	230	210	312	270	246	888
151	138	074	191	174	650	231	211	226	271	247	802
152	138	989	192	175	565	232	212	141	272	248	717
153	139	903	193	176	479	233	213	055	273	249	631
154	140	818	194	177	394	234	213	970	274	250	546
155	141	732	195	178	308	235	214	884	275	251	460
156	142	646	196	179	222	236	215	798	276	252	374
157	143	561	197	180	137	237	216	713	277	253	289
158	144	475	198	181	051	238	217	627	278	254	203
159	145	390	199	181	966	239	218	542	279	255	118
160	146	304	200	182	880	240	219	456	280	256	032

Yds.	metres mm.	Yds.	metres mm.	Yds.	metres mm.	Yds.	metres mm.
281	256 946	321	293 522	361	330 098	500	457 200
282	257 861	322	294 437	362	331 013	600	548 639
283	258 775	323	295 351	363	331 927	700	640 079
234	259 690	324	296 266	364	332 842	800	731 519
285	260 604	325	297 180	365	333 756	900	822 959
286	261 518	326	298 094	366	334 670	1000	914 399
287	262 433	327	299 009	367	335 585	1100	1005 839
288	263 347	328	299 923	368	336 499	1200	1097 279
289	264 262	329	300 838	369	337 414	1300	1188 719
290	265 176	330	301 752	370	338 328	1400	1280 159
291	266 090	331	302 666	371	339 242	1500	1371 599
292	267 005	332	303 581	372	340 157	1600	1463 038
293	267 919	333	304 495	373	341 071	1700	1554 478
294	268 834	334	305 410	374	341 986	1800	1645 918
295	269 748	335	306 324	375	342 900	1900	1737 358
296	270 662	336	307 238	376	343 814	2000	1828 798
297	271 577	337	308 153	377	344 729	2100	1920 238
298	272 491	338	309 067	378	345 643	2200	2011 678
299	273 406	339	309 982	379	346 558	2300	2103 118
300	274 320	340	310 896	380	347 472	2400	2194 558
301	275 234	341	311 810	381	348 386	2500	2285 998
302	276 149	342	312 725	382	349 301	2600	2377 437
303	277 063	343	313 639	383	350 215	2700	2468 877
304	277 978	344	314 554	384	351 130	2800	2560 317
305	278 892	345	315 468	385	352 044	2900	2651 757
306	279 806	346	316 382	386	352 958	3000	2743 197
307	280 721	347	317 297	387	353 873	3200	2926 077
308	281 635	348	318 211	388	354 787	3400	3108 957
309	282 550	349	319 126	389	355 702	3500	3200 397
310	283 464	350	320 040	390	356 616	4000	3657 596
311	284 378	351	320 954	391	357 530	4500	4114 796
312	285 293	352	321 869	392	358 445	5000	4571 995
313	286 207	353	322 783	393	359 359	6000	5486 394
314	287 122	354	323 698	394	360 274	7000	6400 793
315	288 036	355	324 612	395	361 188	8000	7315 192
316	288 950	356	325 526	396	362 102	9000	8229 591
317	289 865	357	326 441	397	363 017	10000	9143 990
318	290 779	358	327 355	398	363 931	15000	13715 985
319	291 694	359	328 270	399	364 846	20000	18287 980
320	292 608	360	329 184	400	365 760	25000	22859 975

MILES – KILOMETRES. (1 Furlong = 1/8 Mile.)

Mls.	=km.	metres	Miles	=km.	metres	Miles	=km.	metres	Miles	=km.	metres
1/8	0	201	21	33	796	61	98	170	101	162	543
1/4	0	402	22	35	405	62	99	779	102	164	153
3/8	0	604	23	37	015	63	101	388	103	165	762
1/2	0	805	24	38	624	64	102	998	104	167	371
5/8	1	006	25	40	234	65	104	607	105	168	981
3/4	1	207	26	41	843	66	106	216	106	170	590
7/8	1	408	27	43	452	67	107	826	107	172	199
1	1	609	28	45	062	68	109	435	108	173	809
1/4	2	012	29	46	671	69	111	044	109	175	418
1/2	2	414	30	48	280	70	112	654	110	177	027
3/4	2	816	31	49	890	71	114	263	111	178	637
2	3	219	32	51	499	72	115	872	112	180	246
1/4	3	621	33	53	108	73	117	482	113	181	855
1/2	4	023	34	54	718	74	119	091	114	183	465
3/4	4	426	35	56	327	75	120	700	115	185	074
3	4	828	36	57	936	76	122	310	116	186	683
1/4	5	230	37	59	546	77	123	919	117	188	293
1/2	5	633	38	61	155	78	125	529	118	189	902
3/4	6	035	39	62	764	79	127	138	119	191	511
4	6	437	40	64	374	80	128	747	120	193	121
1/4	6	840	41	65	983	81	130	357	121	194	730
1/2	7	242	42	67	592	82	131	966	122	196	340
3/4	7	644	43	69	202	83	133	575	123	197	949
5	8	047	44	70	811	84	135	185	124	199	558
1/2	8	851	45	72	420	85	136	794	125	201	168
6	9	656	46	74	030	86	138	403	126	202	777
7	11	265	47	75	639	87	140	013	127	204	386
8	12	875	48	77	248	88	141	622	128	205	996
9	14	484	49	78	858	89	143	231	129	207	605
10	16	093	50	80	467	90	144	841	130	209	214
11	17	703	51	82	076	91	146	450	131	210	824
12	19	312	52	83	686	92	148	059	132	212	433
13	20	921	53	85	295	93	149	669	133	214	042
14	22	531	54	86	904	94	151	278	134	215	652
15	24	140	55	88	514	95	152	887	135	217	261
16	25	749	56	90	123	96	154	497	136	218	870
17	27	359	57	91	732	97	156	106	137	220	480
18	28	968	58	93	342	98	157	715	138	222	089
19	30	577	59	94	951	99	159	325	139	223	698
20	32	187	60	96	560	100	160	934	140	225	308

BRITISH
SQUARE AND CUBIC
MEASURES

CONVERTED INTO METRIC.

Contractions.[2]

Contractions[3].		Plural[3]=	Contractions[3].		Plural[3]=
a.c.	... =acre ;	(acres)	hect. ... =hectares ;		
c., cu., cub.	=cubic ;		in., ins. =inch		(inches)
c.c.	... =cubic centimetres ;		m., met. =metres ;		
cm.	=centimetres ;		s., sq. =square ;		
dc.,dec.,deci.	=decimetres ;		yd. =yard ;		(yards)
ft. ...	=foot ;	(feet)			

II.

MESURES DE SUPERFICIE ET DE VOLUME converties en mesures metriques.

ENGLISCHE QUADRATMASSE UND KUBIKMASSE zu metrischen umgerechnet.

MISURE INGLESI DI SUPERFICIE E DI VOLUME convertite in misure metriche.

MEDIDAS CUADRADAS Y CUBICAS INGLESAS convertidas al sistema metrico.

Français.	Deutsch.	Italiano.	Español.
[1] Pages.	[1] Zeiten.	[1] Pagini.	[1] Paginas.
[2] Contraction.	[2] Abkürzungen.	[2] Contrazione.	[2] Contracciones.
[3] Pluriel.	[3] Mehrzahl.	[3] Plurale.	[3] Plural.

SQUARE FEET — SQUARE METRES.

sq.ft.	sq.m.	sq.deci.	sq.ft.	sq.m.	sq.deci.	sq.ft.	sq.m.	sq.deci.	sq.ft.	sq.m.	sq.dec.
1	0	09·3	41	3	80·9	81	7	52·5	121	11	24·1
2	0	18·6	42	3	90·2	82	7	61·8	122	11	33·4
3	0	27·9	43	3	99·5	83	7	71·1	123	11	42·7
4	0	37·2	44	4	08·8	84	7	80·4	124	11	52·0
5	0	46·5	45	4	18·1	85	7	89·7	125	11	61·3
6	0	55·7	46	4	27·4	86	7	99·0	126	11	70·6
7	0	65·0	47	4	36·6	87	8	08·3	127	11	79·9
8	0	74·3	48	4	45·9	88	8	17·5	128	11	89·2
9	0	83·6	49	4	55·2	89	8	26·8	129	11	98·4
10	0	92·9	50	4	64·5	90	8	36·1	130	12	07·7
11	1	02·2	51	4	73·8	91	8	45·4	131	12	17·0
12	1	11·5	52	4	83·1	92	8	54·7	132	12	26·3
13	1	20·8	53	4	92·4	93	8	64·0	133	12	35·6
14	1	30·1	54	5	01·7	94	8	73·3	134	12	44·9
15	1	39·4	55	5	11·0	95	8	82·6	135	12	54·2
16	1	48·6	56	5	20·3	96	8	91·9	136	12	63·5
17	1	57·9	57	5	29·5	97	9	01·2	137	12	72·8
18	1	67·2	58	5	38·8	98	9	10·4	138	12	82·1
19	1	76·5	59	5	48·1	99	9	19·7	139	12	91·4
20	1	85·8	60	5	57·4	100	9	29·0	140	13	00·6
21	1	95·1	61	5	66·7	101	9	38·3	141	13	09·9
22	2	04·4	62	5	76·0	102	9	47·6	142	13	19·2
23	2	13·7	63	5	85·3	103	9	56·9	143	13	28·5
24	2	23·0	64	5	94·6	104	9	66·2	144	13	37·8
25	2	32·3	65	6	03·9	105	9	75·5	145	13	47·1
26	2	41·5	66	6	13·2	106	9	84·8	146	13	56·4
27	2	50·8	67	6	22·5	107	9	94·1	147	13	65·7
28	2	60·1	68	6	31·7	108	10	03·4	148	13	75·0
29	2	69·4	69	6	41·0	109	10	12·6	149	13	84·3
30	2	78·7	70	6	50·3	110	10	21·9	150	13	93·5
31	2	88·0	71	6	59·6	111	10	31·2	151	14	02·8
32	2	97·3	72	6	68·9	112	10	40·5	152	14	12·1
33	3	06·6	73	6	78·2	113	10	49·8	153	14	21·4
34	3	15·9	74	6	87·5	114	10	59·1	154	14	30·7
35	3	25·2	75	6	96·8	115	10	68·4	155	14	40·0
36	3	34·5	76	7	06·1	116	10	77·7	156	14	49·3
37	3	43·7	77	7	15·4	117	10	87·0	157	14	58·6
38	3	53·0	78	7	24·6	118	10	96·3	158	14	67·9
39	3	62·3	79	7	33·9	119	11	05·5	159	14	77·2
40	3	71·6	80	7	43·2	120	11	14·8	160	14	86·4

sq. ft.	sq.m. sq.deci.	sq. ft.	sq.m. sq.deci.	sq. ft.	sq.m. sq.dec.	sq. ft.	sq.m. sq.de.
161	14 95·7	201	18 67·4	250	23 23	4100	380 90
162	15 05·0	202	18 76·6	272	25 27	4200	390 19
163	15 14·3	203	18 85·9	300	27 87	4300	399 48
164	15 23·6	204	18 95·2	400	37 16	4400	408 77
165	15 32·9	205	19 04·5	500	46 45	4500	418 06
166	15 42·2	206	19 13·8	600	55 74	4600	427 35
167	15 51·5	207	19 23·1	700	65 03	4700	436 64
168	15 60·8	208	19 32·4	800	74 32	4800	445 93
169	15 70·1	209	19 41·7	900	83 61	4900	455 22
170	15 79·4	210	19 51·0	1000	92 90	5000	464 51
171	15 88·6	211	19 60·3	1100	102 19	5100	473 80
172	15 97·9	212	19 69·5	1200	111 48	5200	483 10
173	16 07·2	213	19 78·8	1300	120 77	5300	492 39
174	16 16·5	214	19 88·1	1400	130 06	5400	501 68
175	16 25·8	215	19 97·4	1500	139 35	5500	510 97
176	16 35·1	216	20 06·7	1600	148 64	5600	520 26
177	16 44·4	217	20 16·0	1700	157 93	5700	529 55
178	16 53·7	218	20 25·3	1800	167 23	5800	538 84
179	16 63·0	219	20 34·6	1900	176 52	5900	548 13
180	16 72·3	220	20 43·9	2000	185 81	6000	557 42
181	16 81·5	221	20 53·2	2100	195 10	6100	566 71
182	16 90·8	222	20 62·4	2200	204 39	6200	576 00
183	17 00·1	223	20 71·7	2300	213 68	6300	585 29
184	17 09·4	224	20 81·0	2400	222 97	6400	594 58
185	17 18·7	225	20 90·3	2500	232 26	6500	603 87
186	17 28·0	226	20 99·6	2600	241 55	6600	613 16
187	17 37·3	227	21 08·9	2700	250 84	6700	622 45
188	17 46·6	228	21 18·2	2800	260 13	6800	631 74
189	17 55·9	229	21 27·5	2900	269 42	6900	641 03
190	17 65·2	230	21 36·8	3000	278 71	7000	650 32
191	17 74·4	231	21 46·1	3100	288 00		
192	17 83·7	232	21 55·3	3200	297 29		
193	17 93·0	233	21 64·6	3300	306 58		
194	18 02·3	234	21 73·9	3400	315 87		
195	18 11·6	235	21 83·2	3500	325 16		
196	18 20·9	236	21 92·5	3600	334 45		
197	18 30·2	237	22 01·8	3700	343 74		
198	18 39·5	238	22 11·1	3800	353 03		
199	18 48·8	239	22 20·4	3900	362 32		
200	18 58·1	240	22 29·7	4000	371 61		

sq. ft.	s.m. sq.deci
$\frac{1}{12}$	0 00·8
$\frac{2}{12}$	0 01·6
$\frac{1}{4} = \frac{3}{12}$	0 02·3
$\frac{4}{12}$	0 03·1
$\frac{5}{12}$	0 03·9
$\frac{1}{2} \frac{6}{12}$	0 04·7
$\frac{7}{12}$	0 05·4
$\frac{8}{12}$	0 06·2
$\frac{3}{4} = \frac{9}{12}$	0 07·0
$\frac{10}{12}$	0 07·7
$\frac{11}{12}$	0 08·5

SQUARE YARDS – SQUARE METRES.

sq.yd	sq.m.	sq.deci.	sq.yd.	sq.m.	sq.deci.	sq.yd.	sq.m.	sq.deci.	sq.yd.	sq.m.	sq.dec.
1	0	83·6	41	34	28·1	81	67	72·6	121	101	17·1
2	1	67·2	42	35	11·7	82	68	56·2	122	102	00·7
3	2	50·8	43	35	95·3	83	69	39·8	123	102	84·3
4	3	34·5	44	36	79·0	84	70	23·5	124	103	68·0
5	4	18·1	45	37	62·6	85	71	07·1	125	104	51·6
6	5	01·7	46	38	46·2	86	71	90·7	126	105	35·2
7	5	85·3	47	39	29·8	87	72	74·3	127	106	18·8
8	6	68·9	48	40	13·4	88	73	57·9	128	107	02·4
9	7	52·5	49	40	97·0	89	74	41·5	129	107	86·0
10	8	36·1	50	41	80·6	90	75	25·1	130	108	69·6
11	9	19·7	51	42	64·2	91	76	08·7	131	109	53·3
12	10	03·4	52	43	47·9	92	76	92·4	132	110	36·9
13	10	87·0	53	44	31·5	93	77	76·0	133	111	20·5
14	11	70·6	54	45	15·1	94	78	59·6	134	112	04·1
15	12	54·2	55	45	98·7	95	79	43·2	135	112	87·7
16	13	37·8	56	46	82·3	96	80	26·8	136	113	71·3
17	14	21·4	57	47	65·9	97	81	10·4	137	114	54·9
18	15	05·0	58	48	49·5	98	81	94·0	138	115	38·5
19	15	88·6	59	49	33·1	99	82	77·6	139	116	22·2
20	16	72·3	60	50	16·8	100	83	61·3	140	117	05·8
21	17	55·9	61	51	00·4	101	84	44·9	141	117	89·4
22	18	39·5	62	51	84·0	102	85	28·5	142	118	73·0
23	19	23·1	63	52	67·6	103	86	12·1	143	119	56·6
24	20	06·7	64	53	51·2	104	86	95·7	144	120	40·2
25	20	90·3	65	54	34·8	105	87	79·3	145	121	23·8
26	21	73·9	66	55	18·4	106	88	62·9	146	122	07·4
27	22	57·5	67	56	02·0	107	89	46·5	147	122	91·1
28	23	41·2	68	56	85·7	108	90	30·2	148	123	74·7
29	24	24·8	69	57	69·3	109	91	13·8	149	124	58·3
30	25	08·4	70	58	52·9	110	91	97·4	150	125	41·9
31	25	92·0	71	59	36·5	111	92	81·0	151	126	25·5
32	26	75·6	72	60	20·1	112	93	64·6	152	127	09·1
33	27	59·2	73	61	03·7	113	94	48·2	153	127	92·7
34	28	42·8	74	61	87·3	114	95	31·8	154	128	76·3
35	29	26·4	75	62	70·9	115	96	15·4	155	129	60·0
36	30	10·1	76	63	54·6	116	96	99·1	156	130	43·6
37	30	93·7	77	64	38·2	117	97	82·7	157	131	27·2
38	31	77·3	78	65	21·8	118	98	66·3	158	132	10·8
39	32	60·9	79	66	05·4	119	99	49·9	159	132	94·4
40	33	44·5	80	66	89·0	120	100	33·5	160	133	78·0

sq. yd.	sq.m. sq.deci.	sq. yd.	sq.m. sq.deci.	sq. yd.	sq.m. sq.deci.	sq. yd.	sq.m. sq.de.
161	134 61·6	201	168 06·1	250	209 03	4100	3428 12
162	135 45·2	202	168 89·7	300	250 84	4200	3511 73
163	136 28·9	203	169 73·4	350	292 64	4300	3595 34
164	137 12·5	204	170 57·0	400	334 45	4400	3678 95
165	137 96·1	205	171 40·6	500	418 06	4500	3762 57
166	138 79·7	206	172 24·2	600	501 68	4600	3846 18
167	139 63·3	207	173 07·8	700	585 29	4700	3929 79
168	140 46·9	208	173 91·4	800	668 90	4800	4013 40
169	141 30·5	209	174 75·0	900	752 51	4900	4097 02
170	142 14·1	210	175 58·6	1000	836 13	5000	4180 63
171	142 97·8	211	176 42·3	1100	919 74	5100	4264 24
172	143 81·4	212	177 25·9	1200	1003 35	5200	4347 86
173	144 65·0	213	178 09·5	1300	1086 96	5300	4431 47
174	145 48·6	214	178 93·1	1400	1170 58	5400	4515 08
175	146 32·2	215	179 76·7	1500	1254 19	5500	4598 69
176	147 15·8	216	180 60·3	1600	1337 80	5600	4682 31
177	147 99·4	217	181 43·9	1700	1421 41	5700	4765 92
178	148 83·0	218	182 27·5	1800	1505 03	5800	4849 53
179	149 66·7	219	183 11·2	1900	1588 64	5900	4933 14
180	150 50·3	220	183 94·8	2000	1672 25	6000	5016 76
181	151 33·9	221	184 78·4	2100	1755 86	6100	5100 37
182	152 17·5	222	185 62·0	2200	1839 48	6200	5183 98
183	153 01·1	223	186 45·6	2300	1923 09	6300	5267 59
184	153 84·7	224	187 29·2	2400	2006 70	6400	5351 21
185	154 68·3	225	188 12·8	2500	2090 31	6500	5434 82
186	155 51·9	226	188 96·4	2600	2173 93	6600	5518 43
187	156 35·6	227	189 80·1	2700	2257 54	6700	5602 04
188	157 19·2	228	190 63·7	2800	2341 15	6800	5685 66
189	158 02·8	229	191 47·3	2900	2424 77	6900	5769 27
190	158 86·4	230	192 30·9	3000	2508 38	7000	5852 88
191	159 70·0	231	193 14·5	3100	2591 99	8000	6689 01
192	160 53·6	232	193 98·1	3200	2675 60	9000	7525 13
193	161 37·2	233	194 81·7	3300	2759 22	10000	8361 26
194	162 20·8	234	195 65·3	3400	2842 83		
195	163 04·5	235	196 49·0	3500	2926 44		
196	163 88·1	236	197 32·6	3600	3010 05		
197	164 71·7	237	198 16·2	3700	3093 67		
198	165 55·3	238	198 99·8	3800	3177 28		
199	166 38·9	239	199 83·4	3900	3260 89		
200	167 22·5	240	200 67·0	4000	3344 50		

sq. yd.	s.m. sq.deci.
1/8	0 10·5
1/4	0 20·9
3/8	0 31·4
1/2	0 41·8
5/8	0 52·3
3/4	0 62·7
7/8	0 73·2

20. SQ. INCHES = SQ. DECIMETRES & SQ. CENTIMETRES.

Sq. in.	s.deci.	sq. cm.	Sq. in.	s.deci.	sq. cm.	Sq. in.	s.deci.	sq. cm.	Sq. in.	s.deci.	sq. c.
1	0	06·45	37	2	38·71	73	4	70·97	109	7	03·22
2	0	12·90	38	2	45·16	74	4	77·42	110	7	09·68
3	0	19·35	39	2	51·61	75	4	83·87	111	7	16·13
4	0	25·81	40	2	58·06	76	4	90·32	112	7	22·58
5	0	32·26	41	2	64·52	77	4	96·77	113	7	29·03
6	0	38·71	42	2	70·97	78	5	03·22	114	7	35·48
7	0	45·16	43	2	77·42	79	5	09·68	115	7	41·93
8	0	51·61	44	2	83·87	80	5	16·13	116	7	48·39
9	0	58·06	45	2	90·32	81	5	22·58	117	7	54·84
10	0	64·52	46	2	96·77	82	5	29·03	118	7	61·29
11	0	70·97	47	3	03·23	83	5	35·48	119	7	67·74
12	0	77·42	48	3	09·68	84	5	41·93	120	7	74·19
13	0	83·87	49	3	16·13	85	5	48·39	121	7	80·64
14	0	90·32	50	3	22·58	86	5	54·84	122	7	87·10
15	0	96·77	51	3	29·03	87	5	61·29	123	7	93·55
16	1	03·23	52	3	35·48	88	5	67·74	124	8	00·00
17	1	09·68	53	3	41·93	89	5	74·19	125	8	06·45
18	1	16·13	54	3	48·39	90	5	80·64	126	8	12·90
19	1	22·58	55	3	54·84	91	5	87·10	127	8	19·35
20	1	29·03	56	3	61·29	92	5	93·55	128	8	25·80
21	1	35·48	57	3	67·74	93	6	00·00	129	8	32·26
22	1	41·94	58	3	74·19	94	6	06·45	130	8	38·71
23	1	48·39	59	3	80·64	95	6	12·90	131	8	45·16
24	1	54·84	60	3	87·10	96	6	19·35	132	8	51·61
25	1	61·29	61	3	93·55	97	6	25·81	133	8	58·06
26	1	67·74	62	4	00·00	98	6	32·26	134	8	64·51
27	1	74·19	63	4	06·45	99	6	38·71	135	8	70·97
28	1	80·64	64	4	12·90	100	6	45·16	136	8	77·42
29	1	87·10	65	4	19·35	101	6	51·61	137	8	83·87
30	1	93·55	66	4	25·81	102	6	58·06	138	8	90·32
31	2	00·00	67	4	32·26	103	6	64·51	139	8	96·77
32	2	06·45	68	4	38·71	104	6	70·97	140	9	03·22
33	2	12·90	69	4	45·16	105	6	77·42	141	9	09·68
34	2	19·35	70	4	51·61	106	6	83·87	142	9	16·13
35	2	25·81	71	4	58·06	107	6	90·32	143	9	22·58
36	2	32·26	72	4	64·52	108	6	96·77	144	9	29·03
200	12	90·32	600	38	70·96	1000	64	51·60	1368	88	25·79
300	19	35·48	700	45	16·12	1200	77	41·92	1400	90	32·24
400	25	80·64	800	51	61·28	1224	78	96·76	1500	96	77·40
500	32	25·80	900	58	06·44	1296	83	61·27	2000	129	03·20

Ac.	hect.	ares	sq.m	Acres	hect.	ares	sq.m	Acres	hect.	ares	sq.m	Acres	hect.	ares	sq.m
¼	0	10	12	11	4	45	15	51	20	63	89	91	36	82	63
½	0	20	23	12	4	85	62	52	21	04	36	92	37	23	10
¾	0	30	35	13	5	26	09	53	21	44	83	93	37	63	57
1	0	40	47	14	5	66	56	54	21	85	30	94	38	04	04
¼	0	50	59	15	6	07	03	55	22	25	77	95	38	44	51
½	0	60	70	16	6	47	50	56	22	66	23	96	38	84	97
¾	0	70	82	17	6	87	96	57	23	06	70	97	39	25	44
2	0	80	94	18	7	28	43	58	23	47	17	98	39	65	91
¼	0	91	05	19	7	68	90	59	23	87	64	99	40	06	38
½	1	01	17	20	8	09	37	60	24	28	11	100	40	46	85
¾	1	11	29	21	8	49	84	61	24	68	58	101	40	87	32
3	1	21	41	22	8	90	31	62	25	09	05	102	41	27	79
¼	1	31	52	23	9	30	77	63	25	49	51	103	41	68	25
½	1	41	64	24	9	71	24	64	25	89	98	104	42	08	72
¾	1	51	76	25	10	11	71	65	26	30	45	105	42	49	19
4	1	61	87	26	10	52	18	66	26	70	92	106	42	89	66
¼	1	71	99	27	10	92	65	67	27	11	39	107	43	30	13
½	1	82	11	28	11	33	12	68	27	51	86	108	43	70	60
¾	1	92	23	29	11	73	59	69	27	92	32	109	44	11	06
5	2	02	34	30	12	14	05	70	28	32	79	110	44	51	53
¼	2	12	46	31	12	54	52	71	28	73	26	111	44	92	00
½	2	22	58	32	12	94	99	72	29	13	73	112	45	32	47
¾	2	32	69	33	13	35	46	73	29	54	20	113	45	72	94
6	2	42	81	34	13	75	93	74	29	94	67	114	46	13	41
¼	2	52	93	35	14	16	40	75	30	35	14	115	46	53	87
½	2	63	05	36	14	56	87	76	30	75	60	116	46	94	34
¾	2	73	16	37	14	97	33	77	31	16	07	117	47	34	81
7	2	83	28	38	15	37	80	78	31	56	54	118	47	75	28
¼	2	93	40	39	15	78	27	79	31	97	01	119	48	15	75
½	3	03	51	40	16	18	74	80	32	37	48	120	48	56	22
¾	3	13	63	41	16	59	21	81	32	77	95	130	52	60	90
8	3	23	75	42	16	99	68	82	33	18	42	140	56	65	59
¼	3	33	86	43	17	40	14	83	33	58	88	150	60	70	27
½	3	43	98	44	17	80	61	84	33	99	35	160	64	74	96
¾	3	54	10	45	18	21	08	85	34	39	82	170	68	79	64
9	3	64	22	46	18	61	55	86	34	80	29	180	72	84	33
¼	3	74	33	47	19	02	02	87	35	20	76	190	76	89	01
½	3	84	45	48	19	42	49	88	35	61	23	200	80	93	70
¾	3	94	57	49	19	82	96	89	36	01	69	300	121	40	54
10	4	04	68	50	20	23	42	90	36	42	16	400	161	87	39
												500	202	34	24

CUBE FEET — CUBE METRES.

cu.ft.	cu.m.	cu.deci.	cub.ft.	cu.m.	cu.deci.	cub.ft.	cu.m.	cu.deci.	cub.ft.	cu.m.	c.dec.
1	0	028	41	1	161	81	2	294	121	3	426
2	0	057	42	1	189	82	2	322	122	3	455
3	0	085	43	1	218	83	2	350	123	3	483
4	0	113	44	1	246	84	2	379	124	3	511
5	0	142	45	1	274	85	2	407	125	3	540
6	0	170	46	1	303	86	2	435	126	3	568
7	0	198	47	1	331	87	2	464	127	3	596
8	0	227	48	1	359	88	2	492	128	3	625
9	0	255	49	1	388	89	2	520	129	3	653
10	0	283	50	1	416	90	2	549	130	3	681
11	0	311	51	1	444	91	2	577	131	3	710
12	0	340	52	1	472	92	2	605	132	3	738
13	0	368	53	1	501	93	2	633	133	3	766
14	0	396	54	1	529	94	2	662	134	3	794
15	0	425	55	1	557	95	2	690	135	3	823
16	0	453	56	1	586	96	2	718	136	3	851
17	0	481	57	1	614	97	2	747	137	3	879
18	0	510	58	1	642	98	2	775	138	3	908
19	0	538	59	1	671	99	2	803	139	3	936
20	0	566	60	1	699	100	2	832	140	3	964
21	0	595	61	1	727	101	2	860	141	3	993
22	0	623	62	1	756	102	2	888	142	4	021
23	0	651	63	1	784	103	2	917	143	4	049
24	0	680	64	1	812	104	2	945	144	4	078
25	0	708	65	1	841	105	2	973	145	4	106
26	0	736	66	1	869	106	3	002	146	4	134
27	0	765	67	1	897	107	3	030	147	4	163
28	0	793	68	1	926	108	3	058	148	4	191
29	0	821	69	1	954	109	3	087	149	4	219
30	0	850	70	1	982	110	3	115	150	4	248
31	0	878	71	2	011	111	3	143	151	4	276
32	0	906	72	2	039	112	3	172	152	4	304
33	0	934	73	2	067	113	3	200	153	4	333
34	0	963	74	2	095	114	3	228	154	4	361
35	0	991	75	2	124	115	3	256	155	4	389
36	1	019	76	2	152	116	3	285	156	4	417
37	1	048	77	2	180	117	3	313	157	4	446
38	1	076	78	2	209	118	3	341	158	4	474
39	1	104	79	2	237	119	3	370	159	4	502
40	1	133	80	2	265	120	3	398	160	4	531

cu. ft.	c.m.	cu.dec.	cu. ft.	c.m.	cu.dec.	cub. ft.	cu.m.	cu.deci.	cub. ft.	c.m.	cu.deci.
161	4	559	201	5	692	250	7	079	4100	116	100
162	4	587	202	5	720	300	8	495	4200	118	931
163	4	616	203	5	748	350	9	911	4300	121	763
164	4	644	204	5	777	400	11	327	4400	124	595
165	4	672	205	5	805	500	14	159	4500	127	427
166	4	701	206	5	833	600	16	990	4600	130	258
167	4	729	207	5	862	700	19	822	4700	133	090
168	4	757	208	5	890	800	22	654	4800	135	922
169	4	786	209	5	918	900	25	485	4900	138	753
170	4	814	210	5	947	1000	28	317	5000	141	585
171	4	842	211	5	975	1100	31	149	5100	144	417
172	4	871	212	6	003	1200	33	980	5200	147	248
173	4	899	213	6	032	1300	36	812	5300	150	080
174	4	927	214	6	060	1400	39	644	5400	152	912
175	4	955	215	6	088	1500	42	476	5500	155	744
176	4	984	216	6	116	1600	45	307	5600	158	575
177	5	012	217	6	145	1700	48	139	5700	161	407
178	5	040	218	6	173	1800	50	971	5800	164	239
179	5	069	219	6	201	1900	53	802	5900	167	070
180	5	097	220	6	230	2000	56	634	6000	169	902
181	5	125	221	6	258	2100	59	466	6100	172	734
182	5	154	222	6	286	2200	62	297	6200	175	565
183	5	182	223	6	315	2300	65	129	6300	178	397
184	5	210	224	6	343	2400	67	961	6400	181	229
185	5	239	225	6	371	2500	70	793	6500	184	061
186	5	267	226	6	400	2600	73	624	6600	186	892
187	5	295	227	6	428	2700	76	456	6700	189	724
188	5	324	228	6	456	2800	79	288	6800	192	556
189	5	352	229	6	485	2900	82	119	6900	195	387
190	5	380	230	6	513	3000	84	951	7000	198	219
191	5	409	231	6	541	3100	87	783			
192	5	437	232	6	570	3200	90	614			
193	5	465	233	6	598	3300	93	446			
194	5	493	234	6	626	3400	96	278			
195	5	522	235	6	654	3500	99	110			
196	5	550	236	6	683	3600	101	941			
197	5	578	237	6	711	3700	104	773			
198	5	607	238	6	739	3800	107	605			
199	5	635	239	6	768	3900	110	436			
200	5	663	240	6	796	4000	113	268			

cub. ft.	cu.m.	cu.dec.
$\frac{1}{12}$	0	002
$\frac{2}{12}$	0	005
$\frac{1}{4} = \frac{3}{12}$	0	007
$\frac{4}{12}$	0	009
$\frac{5}{12}$	0	012
$\frac{1}{2} \frac{6}{12}$	0	014
$\frac{7}{12}$	0	017
$\frac{8}{12}$	0	019
$\frac{3}{4} = \frac{9}{12}$	0	021
$\frac{10}{12}$	0	024
$\frac{11}{12}$	0	026

CUBE YARDS – CUBE METRES.

c. yd	cu.m.	cu.deci.	cu.yd.	cu.m.	cu.deci.	cub.yd.	cu.m.	cu.deci.	cub.yd.	cu.m.	cu.deci.
1	0	·765	41	31	·347	81	61	·929	121	92	·511
2	1	·529	42	32	·111	82	62	·693	122	93	·275
3	2	·294	43	32	·876	83	63	·458	123	94	·040
4	3	·058	44	33	·640	84	64	·222	124	94	·805
5	3	·823	45	34	·405	85	64	·987	125	95	·569
6	4	·587	46	35	·169	86	65	·752	126	96	·334
7	5	·352	47	35	·934	87	66	·516	127	97	·098
8	6	·116	48	36	·699	88	67	·281	128	97	·863
9	6	·881	49	37	·463	89	68	·045	129	98	·627
10	7	·646	50	38	·228	90	68	·810	130	99	·392
11	8	·410	51	38	·992	91	69	·574	131	100	·156
12	9	·175	52	39	·757	92	70	·339	132	100	·921
13	9	·939	53	40	·521	93	71	·103	133	101	·686
14	10	·704	54	41	·286	94	71	·868	134	102	·450
15	11	·468	55	42	·050	95	72	·633	135	103	·215
16	12	·233	56	42	·815	96	73	·397	136	103	·979
17	12	·997	57	43	·580	97	74	·162	137	104	·744
18	13	·762	58	44	·344	98	74	·926	138	105	·508
19	14	·527	59	45	·109	99	75	·691	139	106	·273
20	15	·291	60	45	·873	100	76	·455	140	107	·037
21	16	·056	61	46	·638	101	77	·220	141	107	·802
22	16	·820	62	47	·402	102	77	·984	142	108	·567
23	17	·585	63	48	·167	103	78	·749	143	109	·331
24	18	·349	64	48	·931	104	79	·514	144	110	·096
25	19	·114	65	49	·696	105	80	·278	145	110	·860
26	19	·878	66	50	·460	106	81	·043	146	111	·625
27	20	·643	67	51	·225	107	81	·807	147	112	·389
28	21	·407	68	51	·990	108	82	·572	148	113	·154
29	22	·172	69	52	·754	109	83	·336	149	113	·918
30	22	·937	70	53	·519	110	84	·101	150	114	·683
31	23	·701	71	54	·283	111	84	·865	151	115	·448
32	24	·466	72	55	·048	112	85	·630	152	116	·212
33	25	·230	73	55	·812	113	86	·394	153	116	·977
34	25	·995	74	56	·577	114	87	·159	154	117	·741
35	26	·759	75	57	·341	115	87	·924	155	118	·506
36	27	·524	76	58	·106	116	88	·688	156	119	·270
37	28	·288	77	58	·871	117	89	·453	157	120	·035
38	29	·053	78	59	·635	118	90	·217	158	120	·799
39	29	·818	79	60	·400	119	90	·982	159	121	·564
40	30	·582	80	61	·164	120	91	·746	160	122	·328

cu. yd.	cu.m. cu.dec.	cu. yd.	cu.m. cu.dec.	cub. yd.	cu.m. cu.deci.	cub.yd.	cu.m. cu.deci.
161	123 093	201	153 675	250	191 138	4100	3134 667
162	123 858	202	154 440	300	229 366	4200	3211 123
163	124 622	203	155 204	350	267 594	4300	3287 578
164	125 387	204	155 969	400	305 821	4400	3364 033
165	126 151	205	156 733	500	382 277	4500	3440 489
166	126 916	206	157 498	600	458 732	4600	3516 944
167	127 680	207	158 262	700	535 187	4700	3593 399
168	128 445	208	159 027	800	611 642	4800	3669 854
169	129 209	209	159 792	900	688 098	4900	3746 310
170	129 974	**210**	160 556	**1000**	764 553	**5000**	3822 765
171	130 739	211	161 321	1100	841 008	5100	3899 220
172	131 503	212	162 085	1200	917 464	5200	3975 676
173	132 268	213	162 850	1300	993 919	5300	4052 131
174	133 032	214	163 614	1400	1070 374	5400	4128 586
175	133 797	215	164 379	1500	1146 830	5500	4205 042
176	134 561	216	165 143	1600	1223 285	5600	4281 497
177	135 326	217	165 908	1700	1299 740	5700	4357 952
178	136 090	218	166 673	1800	1376 195	5800	4434 407
179	136 855	219	167 437	1900	1452 651	5900	4510 863
180	137 620	**220**	168 202	**2000**	1529 106	**6000**	4587 318
181	138 384	221	168 966	2100	1605 561	6100	4663 773
182	139 149	222	169 731	2200	1682 017	6200	4740 229
183	139 913	223	170 495	2300	1758 472	6300	4816 684
184	140 678	224	171 260	2400	1834 927	6400	4893 139
185	141 442	225	172 024	2500	1911 383	6500	4969 595
186	142 207	226	172 789	2600	1987 838	6600	5046 050
187	142 971	227	173 554	2700	2064 293	6700	5122 505
188	143 736	228	174 318	2800	2140 748	6800	5198 960
189	144 501	229	175 083	2900	2217 204	6900	5275 416
190	145 265	**230**	175 847	**3000**	2293 659	**7000**	5351 871
191	146 030	231	176 612	3100	2370 114	8000	6116 424
192	146 794	232	177 376	3200	2446 570	9000	6880 977
193	147 559	233	178 141	3300	2523 025	10000	7645 530
194	148 323	234	178 905	3400	2599 480		
195	149 088	235	179 670	3500	2675 936		
196	149 852	236	180 435	3600	2752 391		
197	150 617	237	181 199	3700	2828 846		
198	151 381	238	181 964	3800	2905 301		
199	152 146	239	182 728	3900	2981 757		
200	152 911	**240**	183 493	**4000**	3058 212		

cub. yd.	cu.m. cu.dec.
$\frac{1}{8}$	0 096
$\frac{1}{4}$	0 191
$\frac{3}{8}$	0 287
$\frac{1}{2}$	0 382
$\frac{5}{8}$	0 478
$\frac{3}{4}$	0 573
$\frac{7}{8}$	0 669

C

cub.in.	c.deci.	c.c.	cub.ins.	c.deci.	c.c.	cub. ins.	c.deci.	c.c.	cub. ins.	c.deci.	c.c.
10	0	164	410	6	719	810	13	273	1220	19	992
20	0	328	420	6	883	820	13	437	1240	20	320
30	0	492	430	7	046	830	13	601	1260	20	648
40	0	655	440	7	210	840	13	765	1280	20	975
50	0	819	450	7	374	850	13	929	1300	21	303
60	0	983	460	7	538	860	14	093	1320	21	631
70	1	147	470	7	702	870	14	257	1340	21	959
80	1	311	480	7	866	880	14	421	1360	22	286
90	1	475	490	8	030	890	14	584	1380	22	614
100	1	639	500	8	194	900	14	748	1400	22	942
110	1	803	510	8	357	910	14	912	1420	23	270
120	1	966	520	8	521	920	15	076	1440	23	597
130	2	130	530	8	685	930	15	240	1460	23	925
140	2	294	540	8	849	940	15	404	1480	24	253
150	2	458	550	9	013	950	15	568	1500	24	581
160	2	622	560	9	177	960	15	732	1520	24	908
170	2	786	570	9	341	970	15	895	1540	25	236
180	2	950	580	9	504	980	16	059	1560	25	564
190	3	114	590	9	668	990	16	223	1580	25	891
200	3	277	600	9	832	1000	16	387	1600	26	219
210	3	441	610	9	996	1010	16	551	1620	26	547
220	3	605	620	10	160	1020	16	715	1640	26	875
230	3	769	630	10	324	1030	16	879	1660	27	202
240	3	933	640	10	488	1040	17	042	1680	27	530
250	4	097	650	10	652	1050	17	206	1700	27	858
260	4	261	660	10	815	1060	17	370	1728	28	317
270	4	424	670	10	979	1070	17	534	1800	29	497
280	4	588	680	11	143	1080	17	698	1900	31	135
290	4	752	690	11	307	1090	17	862	2000	32	774
300	4	916	700	11	471	1100	18	026	3000	49	161
310	5	080	710	11	635	1110	18	190			
320	5	244	720	11	799	1120	18	353			
330	5	408	730	11	963	1130	18	517			
340	5	572	740	12	126	1140	18	681			
350	5	735	750	12	290	1150	18	845			
360	5	899	760	12	454	1160	19	009			
370	6	063	770	12	618	1170	19	173			
380	6	227	780	12	782	1180	19	337			
390	6	391	790	12	946	1190	19	501			
400	6	555	800	13	110	1200	19	664			

c.in	c.c.	c.in.	c.c.
1	16·4	11	180·3
2	32·8	12	196·6
3	49·2	13	213·0
4	65·5	14	229·4
5	81·9	15	245·8
6	98·3	16	262·2
7	114·7	17	278·6
8	131·1	18	295·0
9	147·5	19	311·4
10	163·9	20	327·7

United States Measures, see pp. 96-99.

III.

BRITISH
LIQUID AND CAPACITY
MEASURES

CONVERTED INTO METRIC.

Contractions.[2]

Contractions[2].		*Plural*[3]=	Contractions[2].		*Plural*[3]=
Av., Avoir.	=Avoirdupois;		l., lit. ...	=litre;	(litres)
Bsh., Bush.	=bushel;	(bushels)	millilit.		
c.c. ...	=cubic centimetres;		m'lit., m'llilit.	} =millilitres;	
fl. ...	=fluid;		oz., ozs.	=ounce;	(ounces)
gal., gall.	=gallon;	(gallons)	pt. ...	=pint;	(pints)
hect., hecto.	=hectolitres;		qr.	=quarter;	(quarters)

III.

MESURES ANGLAISES DE CAPACITÉ ET LIQUIDES converties en mesures metriques.

ENGLISCHE HOHLMASSE UND FLUSSIGKEITSMASSE zu metrischen umgerechnet.

MISURE INGLESI DI CAPACITA E LIQUIDE convertite in misure metriche.

MEDIDAS LIQUIDAS Y DE CAPACITAD del sistema ingles convertidas al sistema metrico.

Français.	Deutsch.	Italiano.	Español.
[1] Pages.	[1] Zeiten.	[1] Pagini.	[1] Paginas.
[2] Contraction.	[2] Abkürzungen.	[2] Contrazione.	[2] Contracciones.
[3] Pluriel.	[3] Mehrzahl.	[3] Plurale.	[3] Plural.

GALLONS & PINTS — LITRES.

Gal. pt	=lit.	millilit.	Pints	Gal. pt	=lit.	millilit.	Pints	Gal. pt	=lit.	millilit.	Pints
1/8	0	568	1	5.1	23	298	41	10.1	46	028	81
1/4 ...	1	136	2	2	23	866	42	2	46	596	82
3/8	1	705	3	3	24	435	43	3	47	164	83
1/2 ...	2	273	4	4	25	003	44	4	47	733	84
5/8	2	841	5	5	25	571	45	5	48	301	85
3/4 ...	3	409	6	6	26	139	46	6	48	869	86
7/8	3	978	7	³Pecks. 7	26	708	47	7	49	437	87
1. 0	4	546	8	³6.0	27	276	48	11.0	50	006	88
1	5	114	9	1	27	844	49	1	50	574	89
2	5	682	10	2	28	412	50	2	51	142	90
3	6	251	11	3	28	981	51	3	51	710	91
4	6	819	12	4	29	549	52	4	52	279	92
5	7	387	13	5	30	117	53	5	52	847	93
6	7	955	14	6	30	685	54	6	53	415	94
¹Peck. 7	8	524	15	⁶Pecks. 7	31	253	55	⁷Pecks. 7	53	983	95
¹2.0	9	092	16	7. 0	31	822	56	⁶12.0	54	552	96
1	9	660	17	1	32	390	57	1	55	120	97
2	10	228	18	2	32	958	58	2	55	688	98
3	10	797	19	3	33	526	59	3	56	256	99
4	11	365	20	4	34	095	60	4	56	825	100
5	11	933	21	5	34	663	61	5	57	393	101
6	12	501	22	6	35	231	62	6	57	961	102
7	13	070	23	Pecks. 7	35	799	63	7	58	529	103
3. 0	13	638	24	⁴8.0	36	368	64	13.0	59	098	104
1	14	206	25	1	36	936	65	1	59	666	105
2	14	774	26	2	37	504	66	2	60	234	106
3	15	343	27	3	38	072	67	3	60	802	107
4	15	911	28	4	38	641	68	4	61	371	108
5	16	479	29	5	39	209	69	5	61	939	109
6	17	047	30	6	39	777	70	6	62	507	110
²Pecks. 7	17	616	31	7	40	345	71	⁷Pecks. 7	63	075	111
²4.0	18	184	32	9. 0	40	914	72	⁷14.0	63	643	112
1	18	752	33	1	41	482	73	1	64	212	113
2	19	320	34	2	42	050	74	2	64	780	114
3	19	889	35	3	42	618	75	3	65	348	115
4	20	457	36	4	43	187	76	4	65	916	116
5	21	025	37	5	43	755	77	5	66	485	117
6	21	593	38	6	44	323	78	6	67	053	118
7	22	162	39	Pecks. 7	44	891	79	7	67	621	119
5. 0	22	730	40	⁵10.0	45	460	80	15. 0	68	189	120

Gal. pt.	=lit.	millilit.	Pints	Gal. pt.	=lit.	millilit.	Pints	Gallons	=litres	millilit.
15.1	68	758	121	20.1	91	488	161	200	909	193
2	69	326	122	2	92	056	162	252	1145	583
3	69	894	123	3	92	624	163	300	1363	789
4	70	462	124	4	93	192	164	400	1818	385
5	71	031	125	5	93	760	165	500	2272	982
6	71	599	126	6	94	329	166	600	2727	578
7	72	167	127	7	94	897	167	700	3182	174
16.0	72	735	128	21.0	95	465	168	800	3636	770
1	73	304	129	1	96	033	169	900	4091	367
2	73	872	130	2	96	602	170	1000	4545	963
3	74	440	131	3	97	170	171	1100	5000	559
4	75	008	132	4	97	738	172	1200	5455	156
5	75	577	133	5	98	306	173	1300	5909	752
6	76	145	134	6	98	875	174	1400	6364	348
7	76	713	135	7	99	443	175	1500	6818	945
17.0	77	281	136	22.0	100	011	176	1600	7273	541
1	77	850	137	1	100	579	177	1700	7728	137
2	78	418	138	2	101	148	178	1800	8182	734
3	78	986	139	3	101	716	179	1900	8637	330
4	79	554	140	4	102	284	180	2000	9091	926
5	80	123	141	5	102	852	181	2100	9546	523
6	80	691	142	6	103	421	182	2200	10001	119
7	81	259	143	7	103	989	183	2300	10455	715
18.0	81	827	144	23.0	104	557	184	2400	10910	311
1	82	396	145	1	105	125	185	2500	11364	908
2	82	964	146	2	105	694	186	2600	11819	504
3	83	532	147	3	106	262	187	2700	12274	100
4	84	100	148	4	106	830	188	2800	12728	697
5	84	669	149	5	107	398	189	2900	13183	293
6	85	237	150	6	107	967	190	3000	13637	889
7	85	805	151	7	108	535	191	3100	14092	486
19.0	86	373	152	24.0	109	103	192	3200	14547	082
1	86	942	153	1	109	671	193	3300	15001	678
2	87	510	154	2	110	240	194	3400	15456	275
3	88	078	155	3	110	808	195	3500	15910	871
4	88	646	156	4	111	376	196			
5	89	215	157	5	111	944	197			
6	89	783	158	6	112	513	198			
7	90	351	159	7	113	081	199			
20.0	90	919	160	25.0	113	649	200			

Fl.oz	l. m'lit.	Gall.	l. m'lit.
1	0 028	1/6	0 758
Gills	l. mlit.	1/3	1 515
1	0 142	1/2	2 273
2	0 284	2/3	3 031
3	0 426	5/6	3 788

GALLONS & PINTS — LITRES.

Gal. pt.	lit.	millilit.	Pints	Gal. pt.	lit.	millilit.	Pints	Gal. pt.	lit.	millilit.	Pints
25.1	114	217	201	30.1	136	947	241	35.1	159	677	281
2	114	786	202	2	137	515	242	2	160	245	282
3	115	354	203	3	138	084	243	3	160	813	283
4	115	922	204	4	138	652	244	4	161	382	284
5	116	490	205	5	139	220	245	5	161	950	285
6	117	059	206	6	139	788	246	6	162	518	286
7	117	627	207	7	140	357	247	7	163	086	287
26.0	118	195	208	31.0	140	925	248	36.0	163	655	288
1	118	763	209	1	141	493	249	1	164	223	289
2	119	332	210	2	142	061	250	2	164	791	290
3	119	900	211	3	142	630	251	3	165	359	291
4	120	468	212	4	143	198	252	4	165	928	292
5	121	036	213	5	143	766	253	5	166	496	293
6	121	605	214	6	144	334	254	6	167	064	294
7	122	173	215	7	144	903	255	7	167	632	295
27.0	122	741	216	32.0	145	471	256	37.0	168	201	296
1	123	309	217	1	146	039	257	1	168	769	297
2	123	877	218	2	146	607	258	2	169	337	298
3	124	446	219	3	147	176	259	3	169	905	299
4	125	014	220	4	147	744	260	4	170	474	300
5	125	582	221	5	148	312	261	5	171	042	301
6	126	150	222	6	148	880	262	6	171	610	302
7	126	719	223	7	149	449	263	7	172	178	303
28.0	127	287	224	33.0	150	017	264	38.0	172	747	304
1	127	855	225	1	150	585	265	1	173	315	305
2	128	423	226	2	151	153	266	2	173	883	306
3	128	992	227	3	151	722	267	3	174	451	307
4	129	560	228	4	152	290	268	4	175	020	308
5	130	128	229	5	152	858	269	5	175	588	309
6	130	696	230	6	153	426	270	6	176	156	310
7	131	265	231	7	153	995	271	7	176	724	311
29.0	131	833	232	34.0	154	563	272	39.0	177	293	312
1	132	401	233	1	155	131	273	1	177	861	313
2	132	969	234	2	155	699	274	2	178	429	314
3	133	538	235	3	156	267	275	3	178	997	315
4	134	106	236	4	156	836	276	4	179	566	316
5	134	674	237	5	157	404	277	5	180	134	317
6	135	242	238	6	157	972	278	6	180	702	318
7	135	811	239	7	158	540	279	7	181	270	319
30.0	136	379	240	35.0	159	109	280	40.0	181	839	320

Gal.	=litres	milli.	Galls.	=litres	milli.	Galls.	=litres	milli.	Gallons	=litres	milli.
41	186	384	81	368	223	121	550	062	200	909	193
42	190	930	82	372	769	122	554	607	252	1145	583
43	195	476	83	377	315	123	559	153	300	1363	789
44	200	022	84	381	861	124	563	699	400	1818	385
45	204	568	85	386	407	125	568	245	500	2272	982
46	209	114	86	390	953	126	572	791	600	2727	578
47	213	660	87	395	499	127	577	337	700	3182	174
48	218	206	88	400	045	128	581	883	800	3636	770
49	222	752	89	404	591	129	586	429	900	4091	367
50	227	298	90	409	137	130	590	975	1000	4545	963
51	231	844	91	413	683	131	595	521	1100	5000	559
52	236	390	92	418	229	132	600	067	1200	5455	156
53	240	936	93	422	775	133	604	613	1300	5909	752
54	245	482	94	427	321	134	609	159	1400	6364	348
55	250	028	95	431	867	135	613	705	1500	6818	945
56	254	574	96	436	412	136	618	251	1600	7273	541
57	259	120	97	440	958	137	622	797	1700	7728	137
58	263	666	98	445	504	138	627	343	1800	8182	734
59	268	212	99	450	050	139	631	889	1900	8637	330
60	272	758	100	454	596	140	636	435	2000	9091	926
61	277	304	101	459	142	141	640	981	2100	9546	523
62	281	850	102	463	688	142	645	527	2200	10001	119
63	286	396	103	468	234	143	650	073	2300	10455	715
64	290	942	104	472	780	144	654	619	2400	10910	311
65	295	488	105	477	326	145	659	165	2500	11364	908
66	300	034	106	481	872	146	663	711	2600	11819	504
67	304	580	107	486	418	147	668	257	2700	12274	100
68	309	125	108	490	964	148	672	803	2800	12728	697
69	313	671	109	495	510	149	677	349	2900	13183	293
70	318	217	110	500	056	150	681	894	3000	13637	889
71	322	763	111	504	602	151	686	440	3100	14092	486
72	327	309	112	509	148	152	690	986	3200	14547	082
73	331	855	113	513	694	153	695	532	3300	15001	678
74	336	401	114	518	240	154	700	078	3400	15456	275
75	340	947	115	522	786	155	704	624	3500	15910	871
76	345	493	116	527	332	156	709	170	3600	16365	467
77	350	039	117	531	878	157	713	716	3700	16820	063
78	354	585	118	536	424	158	718	262	3800	17274	660
79	359	131	119	540	970	159	722	808	3900	17729	256
80	363	677	120	545	516	160	727	354	4000	18183	852

QUARTERS & BUSHELS — HECTOLITRES.

Qr.bsh.	=hecto.	litres	Bush.	Qr. bsh.	=hecto.	litres	Bush.	Qr. bush.	=hecto.	litres	Bush.
1/8	0	36	1	5.1	14	91	41	10.1	29	46	81
1/4 ...	0	73	2	2	15	27	42	2	29	82	82
3/8	1	09	3	3	15	64	43	3	30	19	83
1/2 ...	1	45	4	4	16	00	44	4	30	55	84
5/8	1	82	5	5	16	37	45	5	30	91	85
3/4 ...	2	18	6	6	16	73	46	6	31	28	86
7/8	2	55	7	7	17	09	47	7	31	64	87
1. 0	2	91	8	6. 0	17	46	48	11. 0	32	00	88
1	3	27	9	1	17	82	49	1	32	37	89
2	3	64	10	2	18	18	50	2	32	73	90
3	4	00	11	3	18	55	51	3	33	09	91
4	4	36	12	4	18	91	52	4	33	46	92
5	4	73	13	5	19	27	53	5	33	82	93
6	5	09	14	6	19	64	54	6	34	19	94
7	5	46	15	7	20	00	55	7	34	55	95
2. 0	5	82	16	7. 0	20	37	56	12. 0	34	91	96
1	6	18	17	1	20	73	57	1	35	28	97
2	6	55	18	2	21	09	58	2	35	64	98
3	6	91	19	3	21	46	59	3	36	00	99
4	7	27	20	4	21	82	60	4	36	37	100
5	7	64	21	5	22	18	61	5	36	73	101
6	8	00	22	6	22	55	62	6	37	09	102
7	8	36	23	7	22	91	63	7	37	46	103
3. 0	8	73	24	8. 0	23	28	64	13. 0	37	82	104
1	9	09	25	1	23	64	65	1	38	19	105
2	9	46	26	2	24	00	66	2	38	55	106
3	9	82	27	3	24	37	67	3	38	91	107
4	10	18	28	4	24	73	68	4	39	28	108
5	10	55	29	5	25	09	69	5	39	64	109
6	10	91	30	6	25	46	70	6	40	00	110
7	11	27	31	7	25	82	71	7	40	37	111
4. 0	11	64	32	9. 0	26	18	72	14. 0	40	73	112
1	12	00	33	1	26	55	73	1	41	10	113
2	12	36	34	2	26	91	74	2	41	46	114
3	12	73	35	3	27	28	75	3	41	82	115
4	13	09	36	4	27	64	76	4	42	19	116
5	13	46	37	5	28	00	77	5	42	55	117
6	13	82	38	6	28	37	78	6	42	91	118
7	14	18	39	7	28	73	79	7	43	28	119
5. 0	14	55	40	10. 0	29	09	80	15. 0	43	64	120

Qr. bsh.	hect. litres	Bush.	Qr. bsh.	hect. litres	Bush.	Qrs.	=hecto. litres	Bush.
15.1	44 00	121	20.1	58 55	161	50	145 47	400
2	44 37	122	2	58 92	162	62½	181 84	500
3	44 73	123	3	59 28	163	75	218 21	600
4	45 10	124	4	59 64	164	87½	254 57	700
5	45 46	125	5	60 01	165	100	290 94	800
6	45 82	126	6	60 37	166	112½	327 31	900
7	46 19	127	7	60 73	167	125	363 68	1000
16.0	46 55	128	21.0	61 10	168	200	581 88	1600
1	46 91	129	1	61 46	169	250	727 35	2000
2	47 28	130	2	61 82	170	300	872 82	2400
3	47 64	131	3	62 19	171	375	1091 03	3000
4	48 01	132	4	62 55	172	400	1163 76	3200
5	48 37	133	5	62 92	173	500	1454 70	4000
6	48 73	134	6	63 28	174	600	1745 64	4800
7	49 10	135	7	63 64	175	625	1818 38	5000
17.0	49 46	136	22.0	64 01	176	700	2036 58	5600
1	49 82	137	1	64 37	177	750	2182 05	6000
2	50 19	138	2	64 73	178	800	2327 52	6400
3	50 55	139	3	65 10	179	900	2618 46	7200
4	50 91	140	4	65 46	180	1000	2909 40	8000
5	51 28	141	5	65 83	181	1100	3200 34	8800
6	51 64	142	6	66 19	182	1200	3491 28	9600
7	52 01	143	7	66 55	183	1300	3782 22	10400
18.0	52 37	144	23.0	66 92	184	1400	4073 16	11200
1	52 73	145	1	67 28	185	1500	4364 10	12000
2	53 10	146	2	67 64	186	1600	4655 04	12800
3	53 46	147	3	68 01	187	1700	4945 98	13600
4	53 82	148	4	68 37	188	1800	5236 92	14400
5	54 19	149	5	68 73	189	1900	5527 86	15200
6	54 55	150	6	69 10	190	2000	5818 80	16000
7	54 91	151	7	69 46	191			
19.0	55 28	152	24.0	69 83	192			
1	55 64	153	1	70 19	193			
2	56 01	154	2	70 55	194			
3	56 37	155	3	70 92	195			
4	56 73	156	4	71 28	196			
5	57 10	157	5	71 64	197			
6	57 46	158	6	72 01	198			
7	57 82	159	7	72 37	199			
20.0	58 19	160	25.0	72 73	200			

Galls.	Pecks	hect.	litres	Bush.
2	1	0	9	¼
4	2	0	18	½
6	3	0	27	¾
8	4	0	36	1
16	8	0	73	2
24	12	1	09	3
32	16	1	45	4
40	20	1	82	5
48	24	2	18	6
56	28	2	55	7

Qr.bsh.	hecto.	litres	Bush.	Qr. bsh.	=hecto.litres		Bush.	Qr. bush.	=hecto.	litres	Bush.
25.1	73	10	201	30.1	87	65	241	35.1	102	19	281
2	73	46	202	2	88	01	242	2	102	56	282
3	73	83	203	3	88	37	243	3	102	92	283
4	74	19	204	4	88	74	244	4	103	28	284
5	74	55	205	5	89	10	245	5	103	65	285
6	74	92	206	6	89	46	246	6	104	01	286
7	75	28	207	7	89	83	247	7	104	37	287
26.0	75	64	208	31.0	90	19	248	36.0	104	74	288
1	76	01	209	1	90	56	249	1	105	10	289
2	76	37	210	2	90	92	250	2	105	47	290
3	76	74	211	3	91	28	251	3	105	83	291
4	77	10	212	4	91	65	252	4	106	19	292
5	77	46	213	5	92	01	253	5	106	56	293
6	77	83	214	6	92	37	254	6	106	92	294
7	78	19	215	7	92	74	255	7	107	28	295
27.0	78	55	216	32.0	93	10	256	37.0	107	65	296
1	78	92	217	1	93	46	257	1	108	01	297
2	79	28	218	2	93	83	258	2	108	38	298
3	79	64	219	3	94	19	259	3	108	74	299
4	80	01	220	4	94	56	260	4	109	10	300
5	80	37	221	5	94	92	261	5	109	47	301
6	80	74	222	6	95	28	262	6	109	83	302
7	81	10	223	7	95	65	263	7	110	19	303
28.0	81	46	224	33.0	96	01	264	38.0	110	56	304
1	81	83	225	1	96	37	265	1	110	92	305
2	82	19	226	2	96	74	266	2	111	28	306
3	82	55	227	3	97	10	267	3	111	65	307
4	82	92	228	4	97	46	268	4	112	01	308
5	83	28	229	5	97	83	269	5	112	38	309
6	83	65	230	6	98	19	270	6	112	74	310
7	84	01	231	7	98	56	271	7	113	10	311
29.0	84	37	232	34.0	98	92	272	39.0	113	47	312
1	84	74	233	1	99	28	273	1	113	83	313
2	85	10	234	2	99	65	274	2	114	19	314
3	85	46	235	3	100	01	275	3	114	56	315
4	85	83	236	4	100	37	276	4	114	92	316
5	86	19	237	5	100	74	277	5	115	28	317
6	86	55	238	6	101	10	278	6	115	65	318
7	86	92	239	7	101	47	279	7	116	01	319
30.0	87	28	240	35.0	101	83	280	40.0	116	38	320

Qrs.	hecto.	litres	Bush.	Qrs.	hecto.	litres	Bush.
41	119	29	328	81	235	66	648
42	122	19	336	82	238	57	656
43	125	10	344	83	241	48	664
44	128	01	352	84	244	39	672
45	130	92	360	85	247	30	680
46	133	83	368	86	250	21	688
47	136	74	376	87	253	12	696
48	139	65	384	88	256	03	704
49	142	56	392	89	258	94	712
50	145	47	400	90	261	85	720
51	148	38	408	91	264	76	728
52	151	29	416	92	267	66	736
53	154	20	424	93	270	57	744
54	157	11	432	94	273	48	752
55	160	02	440	95	276	39	760
56	162	93	448	96	279	30	768
57	165	84	456	97	282	21	776
58	168	75	464	98	285	12	784
59	171	65	472	99	288	03	792
60	174	56	480	100	290	94	800
61	177	47	488	101	293	85	808
62	180	38	496	102	296	76	816
63	183	29	504	103	299	67	824
64	186	20	512	104	302	58	832
65	189	11	520	105	305	49	840
66	192	02	528	106	308	40	848
67	194	93	536	107	311	31	856
68	197	84	544	108	314	22	864
69	200	75	552	109	317	12	872
70	203	66	560	110	320	03	880
71	206	57	568	111	322	94	888
72	209	48	576	112	325	85	896
73	212	39	584	113	328	76	904
74	215	30	592	114	331	67	912
75	218	21	600	115	334	58	920
76	221	11	608	116	337	49	928
77	224	02	616	117	340	40	936
78	226	93	624	118	343	31	944
79	229	84	632	119	346	22	952
80	232	75	640	120	349	13	960

Qrs.	hecto.	litres	Bush.
50	145	47	400
62½	181	84	500
75	218	21	600
87½	254	57	700
100	290	94	800
112½	327	31	900
125	363	68	1000
200	581	88	1600
250	727	35	2000
300	872	82	2400
375	1091	03	3000
400	1163	76	3200
500	1454	70	4000
600	1745	64	4800
625	1818	38	5000
700	2036	58	5600
750	2182	05	6000
800	2327	52	6400
900	2618	46	7200
1000	2909	40	8000
1100	3200	34	8800
1200	3491	28	9600
1300	3782	22	10400
1400	4073	16	11200
1500	4364	10	12000
1600	4655	04	12800
1700	4945	98	13600
1800	5236	92	14400
1900	5527	86	15200
2000	5818	80	16000

Galls.	Pecks	hect.	litres	Bush.
2	1	0	9	¼
4	2	0	18	½
6	3	0	27	¾
8	4	0	36	1
16	8	0	73	2
24	12	1	09	3
32	16	1	45	4
40	20	1	82	5
48	24	2	18	6
56	28	2	55	7

86. FLUID OUNCES (Avoirdupois) = LITRES & C.C.

Fl. oz.	=lit.	c.c.	Fl. oz.	=lit.	c.c.	Fl. oz.	=lit.	c.c.	Fl. oz.	=lit.	c.c.
1	0	28·4	41	1	165	81	2	301	121	3	438
2	0	56·8	42	1	193	82	2	330	122	3	466
3	0	85·2	43	1	222	83	2	358	123	3	495
4	0	113·6	44	1	250	84	2	387	124	3	523
5	0	142·1	45	1	279	85	2	415	125	3	552
6	0	170·5	46	1	307	86	2	443	126	3	580
7	0	198·9	47	1	335	87	2	472	127	3	608
8	0	227·3	48	1	364	88	2	500	128	3	637
9	0	255·7	49	1	392	89	2	529	129	3	665
10	0	284·1	50	1	421	90	2	557	130	3	694
11	0	312·5	51	1	449	91	2	586	131	3	722
12	0	340·9	52	1	477	92	2	614	132	3	750
13	0	369·3	53	1	506	93	2	642	133	3	779
14	0	397·8	54	1	534	94	2	671	134	3	807
15	0	426·2	55	1	563	95	2	699	135	3	836
16	0	454·6	56	1	591	96	2	728	136	3	864
17	0	483·0	57	1	620	97	2	756	137	3	893
18	0	511·4	58	1	648	98	2	784	138	3	921
¹Pints. 19	0	539·8	Pints. 59	1	676	Pints. 99	2	813	Pints. 139	3	949
¹ 20	0	568·2	³ 60	1	705	⁵ 100	2	841	⁷ 140	3	978
21	0	596·7	61	1	733	101	2	870	141	4	006
22	0	625·1	62	1	762	102	2	898	142	4	035
23	0	653·5	63	1	790	103	2	926	143	4	063
24	0	681·9	64	1	818	104	2	955	144	4	091
25	0	710·3	65	1	847	105	2	983	145	4	120
26	0	738·7	66	1	875	106	3	012	146	4	148
27	0	767·1	67	1	904	107	3	040	147	4	177
28	0	795·6	68	1	932	108	3	069	148	4	205
29	0	824·0	69	1	960	109	3	097	149	4	233
30	0	852·4	70	1	989	110	3	125	150	4	262
31	0	880·8	71	2	017	111	3	154	151	4	290
32	0	909·2	72	2	046	112	3	182	152	4	319
33	0	937·6	73	2	074	113	3	211	153	4	347
34	0	966·0	74	2	103	114	3	239	154	4	376
35	0	994·4	75	2	131	115	3	267	155	4	404
36	1	022·8	76	2	159	116	3	296	156	4	432
37	1	051·3	77	2	188	117	3	324	157	4	461
38	1	079·7	78	2	216	118	3	353	158	4	489
Pints. 39	1	108·1	Pints. 79	2	245	Pints. 119	3	381	Pints. 159	4	518
² 40	1	136·5	⁴ 80	2	273	⁶ 120	3	409	⁸ 160	4	546

United States Weights, see pp. 93-95, 100;
Tons @ 1016·047, see p.49.

IV.

BRITISH WEIGHTS

CONVERTED INTO METRIC.

Contractions.[2]

Contraction[2].	Plural[3]=	Contraction[2].	Plural[3]=
Av., Avoir.	=avoirdupois;	mgs. ...	=milligrams ;
c., cwt. ...	=hundredweight;	oz., ozs.	=ounce ; (ounces)
dr. ...	=drachm;(drachms)	q., qrs.	=quarter;(quarters)
drm. ...	=dram ; (drams)	sc., scr. ...	=scruple ; (scruples)
gm. ...	=grams ;	st., stns.	=stone ; (stones)
gr,, grs.	=grain ; (grains)	T., t., tn.	=ton ; (tons)
k., kil., kilo	=kilograms ;	tnns.	=Tonnes
lb., lbs.	=pound ; (pounds)		

IV.

MESURES ANGLAISES DE POIDS converties en mesures metriques.

ENGLISCHE GEWICHTE zu metrischen umgerechnet.

MISURE INGLESI DI PESI convertite in misure metriche.

PESOS INGLESES convertidos al sistema metrico.

Français.	Deutsch.	Italiano.	Español.
[1] Pages.	[1] Zeiten.	[1] Pagini.	[1] Paginas.
[2] Contraction.	[2] Abkürzungen.	[2] Contrazione.	[2] Contracciones.
[3] Pluriel.	[3] Mehrzahl.	[3] Plurale.	[3] Plural.

GRAINS - GRAMS & MILLIGRAMS.

Grs.	gm. mgs.	Grs.	gm. mgs.	Grs.	gm. mgs.	Grs.	gm. mgs.	Grs.	gm. mgs.
1	0 065	41	2 657	81	5 249	121	7 841	161	10 433
2	0 130	42	2 722	82	5 314	122	7 906	162	10 498
3	0 194	43	2 786	83	5 378	123	7 970	163	10 562
4	0 259	44	2 851	84	5 443	124	8 035	164	10 627
5	0 324	45	2 916	85	5 508	125	8 100	165	10 692
6	0 389	46	2 981	86	5 573	126	8 165	166	10 757
7	0 454	47	3 046	87	5 638	127	8 230	167	10 822
8	0 518	48	3 110	88	5 702	128	8 294	168	10 886
9	0 583	49	3 175	89	5 767	129	8 359	169	10 951
10	0 648	50	3 240	90	5 832	130	8 424	170	11 016
11	0 713	51	3 305	91	5 897	131	8 489	171	11 081
12	0 778	52	3 370	92	5 962	132	8 554	172	11 146
13	0 842	53	3 434	93	6 026	133	8 618	173	11 210
14	0 907	54	3 499	94	6 091	134	8 683	174	11 275
15	0 972	55	3 564	95	6 156	135	8 748	175	11 340
16	1 037	56	3 629	96	6 221	136	8 813	176	11 405
17	1 102	57	3 694	97	6 286	137	8 878	177	11 470
18	1 166	58	3 758	98	6 350	138	8 942	178	11 534
19	1 231	59	3 823	99	6 415	139	9 007	179	11 599
20	1 296	60	3 888	100	6 480	140	9 072	180	11 664
21	1 361	61	3 953	101	6 545	141	9 137	181	11 729
22	1 426	62	4 018	102	6 610	142	9 202	182	11 794
23	1 490	63	4 082	103	6 674	143	9 266	183	11 858
24	1 555	64	4 147	104	6 739	144	9 331	184	11 923
25	1 620	65	4 212	105	6 804	145	9 396	185	11 988
26	1 685	66	4 277	106	6 869	146	9 461	186	12 053
27	1 750	67	4 342	107	6 934	147	9 526	187	12 118
28	1 814	68	4 406	108	6 998	148	9 590	188	12 182
29	1 879	69	4 471	109	7 063	149	9 655	189	12 247
30	1 944	70	4 536	110	7 128	150	9 720	190	12 312
31	2 009	71	4 601	111	7 193	151	9 785	191	12 377
32	2 074	72	4 666	112	7 258	152	9 850	192	12 442
33	2 138	73	4 730	113	7 322	153	9 914	193	12 506
34	2 203	74	4 795	114	7 387	154	9 979	194	12 571
35	2 268	75	4 860	115	7 452	155	10 044	195	12 636
36	2 333	76	4 925	116	7 517	156	10 109	196	12 701
37	2 398	77	4 990	117	7 582	157	10 174	197	12 766
38	2 462	78	5 054	118	7 646	158	10 238	198	12 830
39	2 527	79	5 119	119	7 711	159	10 303	199	12 895
40	2 592	80	5 184	120	7 776	160	10 368	200	12 960

Grs.	gms.	mgs.	Grs.	gms.	mgs.	Grs.	gms.	mgs.	Av. oz.	gms.	mgs.
201	13	025	241	15	617	281	18	209	¼	7	087
202	13	090	242	15	682	282	18	274	½	14	175
203	13	154	243	15	746	283	18	338	¾	21	262
204	13	219	244	15	811	284	18	403	1 oz.	28	350
205	13	284	245	15	876	285	18	468	¼	35	437
206	13	349	246	15	941	286	18	533	½	42	524
207	13	414	247	16	006	287	18	598	¾	49	612
208	13	478	248	16	070	288	18	662	2 oz.	56	699
209	13	543	249	16	135	289	18	727	¼	63	786
210	13	608	250	16	200	290	18	792	½	70	874
211	13	673	251	16	265	291	18	857	¾	77	961
212	13	738	252	16	330	292	18	922	3 oz.	85	049
213	13	802	253	16	394	293	18	986	¼	92	136
214	13	867	254	16	459	294	19	051	½	99	223
215	13	932	255	16	524	295	19	116	¾	106	311
216	13	997	256	16	589	296	19	181	4 oz.	113	398
217	14	062	257	16	654	297	19	246	¼	120	485
218	14	126	258	16	718	298	19	310	½	127	573
219	14	191	259	16	783	299	19	375	¾	134	660
220	14	256	260	16	848	300	19	440	5 oz.	141	748
221	14	321	261	16	913	301	19	505	¼	148	835
222	14	386	262	16	978	302	19	570	½	155	922
223	14	450	263	17	042	303	19	634	¾	163	010
224	14	515	264	17	107	304	19	699	6 oz.	170	097
225	14	580	265	17	172	305	19	764	¼	177	185
226	14	645	266	17	237	306	19	829	½	184	272
227	14	710	267	17	302	307	19	894	¾	191	359
228	14	774	268	17	366	308	19	958	7 oz.	198	447
229	14	839	269	17	431	309	20	023	¼	205	534
230	14	904	270	17	496	310	20	088	½	212	621
231	14	969	271	17	561	311	20	153	¾	219	709
232	15	034	272	17	626	312	20	218	8 oz.	226	796
233	15	098	273	17	690	313	20	282	9	255	146
234	15	163	274	17	755	314	20	347	10	283	495
235	15	228	275	17	820	315	20	412	11	311	845
236	15	293	276	17	885	316	20	477	12	340	194
237	15	358	277	17	950	317	20	542	13	368	544
238	15	422	278	18	014	318	20	606	14	396	893
239	15	487	279	18	079	319	20	671	15	425	243
240	15	552	280	18	144	320	20	736	16 oz.	453	592

GRAINS – GRAMS & MILLIGRAMS.

Grs.	gms.	mgs.	Grs.	gms.	mgs.	Grs.	gms.	mgs.	Grs.	gms.	mgs.
321	20	801	361	23	393	401	25	985	441	28	577
322	20	866	362	23	458	402	26	050	442	28	642
323	20	930	363	23	522	403	26	114	443	28	706
324	20	995	364	23	587	404	26	179	444	28	771
325	21	060	365	23	652	405	26	244	445	28	836
326	21	125	366	23	717	406	26	309	446	28	901
327	21	190	367	23	782	407	26	374	447	28	966
328	21	254	368	23	846	408	26	438	448	29	030
329	21	319	369	23	911	409	26	503	449	29	095
330	21	384	370	23	976	410	26	568	450	29	160
331	21	449	371	24	041	411	26	633	451	29	225
332	21	514	372	24	106	412	26	698	452	29	290
333	21	578	373	24	170	413	26	762	453	29	354
334	21	643	374	24	235	414	26	827	454	29	419
335	21	708	375	24	300	415	26	892	455	29	484
336	21	773	376	24	365	416	26	957	456	29	549
337	21	838	377	24	430	417	27	022	457	29	614
338	21	902	378	24	494	418	27	086	458	29	678
339	21	967	379	24	559	419	27	151	459	29	743
340	22	032	380	24	624	420	27	216	460	29	808
341	22	097	381	24	689	421	27	281	461	29	873
342	22	162	382	24	754	422	27	346	462	29	938
343	22	226	383	24	818	423	27	410	463	30	002
344	22	291	384	24	883	424	27	475	464	30	067
345	22	356	385	24	948	425	27	540	465	30	132
346	22	421	386	25	013	426	27	605	466	30	197
347	22	486	387	25	078	427	27	670	467	30	262
348	22	550	388	25	142	428	27	734	468	30	326
349	22	615	389	25	207	429	27	799	469	30	391
350	22	680	390	25	272	430	27	864	470	30	456
351	22	745	391	25	337	431	27	929	471	30	521
352	22	810	392	25	402	432	27	994	472	30	586
353	22	874	393	25	466	433	28	058	473	30	650
354	22	939	394	25	531	434	28	123	474	30	715
355	23	004	395	25	596	435	28	188	475	30	780
356	23	069	396	25	661	436	28	253	476	30	845
357	23	134	397	25	726	437	28	318	477	30	910
358	23	198	398	25	790	438	28	382	478	30	974
359	23	263	399	25	855	439	28	447	479	31	039
360	23	328	400	25	920	440	28	512	480	31	104

Avoirdupois Ozs.			Troy Ounces.			Troy Ounces.			Troy Ounces.		
Oz.	gms.	mgs.	Ozs.	gms.	mgs.	Ozs.	gms.	mgs.	Ozs.	gms.	mgs.
¼	7	087	1	31	103	41	1275	243	81	2519	382
½	14	175	2	62	207	42	1306	346	82	2550	485
¾	21	262	3	93	310	43	1337	450	83	2581	589
1 oz.	28	350	4	124	414	44	1368	553	84	2612	692
¼	35	437	5	155	517	45	1399	657	85	2643	796
½	42	524	6	186	621	46	1430	760	86	2674	899
¾	49	612	7	217	724	47	1461	864	87	2706	003
2 oz.	56	699	8	248	828	48	1492	967	88	2737	106
¼	63	786	9	279	931	49	1524	071	89	2768	210
½	70	874	10	311	035	50	1555	174	90	2799	313
¾	77	961	11	342	138	51	1586	278	91	2830	417
3 oz.	85	049	12	373	242	52	1617	381	92	2861	520
¼	92	136	13	404	345	53	1648	484	93	2892	624
½	99	223	14	435	449	54	1679	588	94	2923	727
¾	106	311	15	466	552	55	1710	691	95	2954	831
4 oz.	113	398	16	497	656	56	1741	795	96	2985	934
¼	120	485	17	528	759	57	1772	898	97	3017	038
½	127	573	18	559	863	58	1804	002	98	3048	141
¾	134	660	19	590	966	59	1835	105	99	3079	245
5 oz.	141	748	20	622	070	60	1866	209	100	3110	348
¼	148	835	21	653	173	61	1897	312	101	3141	452
½	155	922	22	684	277	62	1928	416	102	3172	555
¾	163	010	23	715	380	63	1959	519	103	3203	659
6 oz.	170	097	24	746	484	64	1990	623	104	3234	762
¼	177	185	25	777	587	65	2021	726	105	3265	865
½	184	272	26	808	691	66	2052	830	106	3296	969
¾	191	359	27	839	794	67	2083	933	107	3328	072
7 oz.	198	447	28	870	897	68	2115	037	108	3359	176
¼	205	534	29	902	001	69	2146	140	109	3390	279
½	212	621	30	933	104	70	2177	244	110	3421	383
¾	219	709	31	964	208	71	2208	347	111	3452	486
8 oz.	226	796	32	995	311	72	2239	451	112	3483	590
9	255	146	33	1026	415	73	2270	554	113	3514	693
10	283	495	34	1057	518	74	2301	658	114	3545	797
11	311	845	35	1088	622	75	2332	761	115	3576	900
12	340	194	36	1119	725	76	2363	865	116	3608	004
13	368	544	37	1150	829	77	2394	968	117	3639	107
14	396	893	38	1181	932	78	2426	072	118	3670	211
15	425	243	39	1213	036	79	2457	175	119	3701	314
16	453	592	40	1244	139	80	2488	278	120	3732	418

D

42. OUNCES & DRAMS (Avoir.) — KILOS & GRAMS.

oz.drm	kilo. grams	oz.drm	kilo. grams	oz.drm	kilo. grams	oz.drm	kilo. grams
0. 1	0 1·77	2. 1	0 58·47	4. 1	0 115·17	6. 1	0 171·87
2	0 3·54	2	0 60·24	2	0 116·94	2	0 173·64
3	0 5·32	3	0 62·02	3	0 118·72	3	0 175·42
4	0 7·09	4	0 63·79	4	0 120·49	4	0 177·19
5	0 8·86	5	0 65·56	5	0 122·26	5	0 178·96
6	0 10·63	6	0 67·33	6	0 124·03	6	0 180·73
7	0 12·40	7	0 69·10	7	0 125·80	7	0 182·50
8	0 14·17	8	0 70·87	8	0 127·57	8	0 184·27
9	0 15·95	9	0 72·65	9	0 129·35	9	0 186·05
10	0 17·72	10	0 74·42	10	0 131·12	10	0 187·82
11	0 19·49	11	0 76·19	11	0 132·89	11	0 189·59
12	0 21·26	12	0 77·96	12	0 134·66	12	0 191·36
13	0 23·03	13	0 79·73	13	0 136·43	13	0 193·13
14	0 24·81	14	0 81·51	14	0 138·21	14	0 194·91
15	0 26·58	15	0 83·28	15	0 139·98	15	0 196·68
1. 0	0 28·35	3. 0	0 85·05	5. 0	0 141·75	7. 0	0 198·45
1	0 30·12	1	0 86·82	1	0 143·52	1	0 200·22
2	0 31·89	2	0 88·59	2	0 145·29	2	0 201·99
3	0 33·67	3	0 90·37	3	0 147·07	3	0 203·77
4	0 35·44	4	0 92·14	4	0 148·84	4	0 205·54
5	0 37·21	5	0 93·91	5	0 150·61	5	0 207·31
6	0 38·98	6	0 95·68	6	0 152·38	6	0 209·08
7	0 40·75	7	0 97·45	7	0 154·15	7	0 210·85
8	0 42·52	8	0 99·22	8	0 155·92	8	0 212·62
9	0 44·30	9	0 101·00	9	0 157·70	9	0 214·40
10	0 46·07	10	0 102·77	10	0 159·47	10	0 216·17
11	0 47·84	11	0 104·54	11	0 161·24	11	0 217·94
12	0 49·61	12	0 106·31	12	0 163·01	12	0 219·71
13	0 51·38	13	0 108·08	13	0 164·78	13	0 221·48
14	0 53·16	14	0 109·86	14	0 166·56	14	0 223·26
15	0 54·93	15	0 111·63	15	0 168·33	15	0 225·03
2. 0	0 56·70	4. 0	0 113·40	6. 0	0 170·10	8. 0	0 226·80

Apothecaries'			Weight.			Apothecaries'			Weight—contd.		
dr. sc.	grams.	mgs.	dr. scr.	grams.	mgs.	dr. scr.	grams.	mgs.	Troy oz.	grams.	mgs.
0 1	1	296	3 1	12	960	6 1	24	624	4	124	414
0 2	2	592	3 2	14	256	6 2	25	920	5	155	517
1 0	3	888	4 0	15	552	7 0	27	216	6	186	621
1 1	5	184	4 1	16	848	7 1	28	512	7	217	724
1 2	6	480	4 2	18	144	7 2	29	808	8	248	828
2 0	7	776	5 0	19	440	Troy oz	grams.	mgs.	9	279	931
2 1	9	072	5 1	20	736	1	31	103	10	311	035
2 2	10	368	5 2	22	032	2	62	207	11	342	138
3 0	11	664	6 0	23	328	3	93	310	1lb Troy	373	242

Ozs.	lb. oz	kilos. grams.	Ozs.	lbs.ozs.	kilos. grams.	Ozs.	lbs. oz	kilos. grams.
8¼	...	0 233·89	16¼	1.0¼	0 460·69	24¼	1.8¼	0 687·49
½		0 240·97	½	½	0 467·77	½	½	0 694·57
¾		0 248·06	¾	¾	0 474·86	¾	¾	0 701·66
9	...	0 255·15	17	1.1	0 481·95	25	1.9	0 708·75
¼		0 262·24	¼	¼	0 489·04	¼	¼	0 715·84
½		0 269·32	½	½	0 496·12	½	½	0 722·92
¾		0 276·41	¾	¾	0 503·21	¾	¾	0 730·01
10	...	0 283·50	18	1.2	0 510·30	26	1.10	0 737·10
¼		0 290·59	¼	¼	0 517·39	¼	¼	0 744·19
½		0 297·67	½	½	0 524·47	½	½	0 751·27
¾		0 304·76	¾	¾	0 531·56	¾	¾	0 758·36
11	...	0 311·85	19	1.3	0 538·65	27	1.11	0 765·45
¼		0 318·94	¼	¼	0 545·74	¼	¼	0 772·54
½		0 326·02	½	½	0 552·82	½	½	0 779·62
¾		0 333·11	¾	¾	0 559·91	¾	¾	0 786·71
12	...	0 340·20	20	1.4	0 567·00	28	1.12	0 793·80
¼		0 347·29	¼	¼	0 574·09	¼	¼	0 800·89
½		0 354·37	½	½	0 581·17	½	½	0 807·97
¾		0 361·46	¾	¾	0 588·26	¾	¾	0 815·06
13	...	0 368·55	21	1.5	0 595·35	29	1.13	0 822·15
¼		0 375·64	¼	¼	0 602·44	¼	¼	0 829·24
½		0 382·72	½	½	0 609·52	½	½	0 836·32
¾		0 389·81	¾	¾	0 616·61	¾	¾	0 843·41
14	...	0 396·90	22	1.6	0 623·70	30	1.14	0 850·50
¼		0 403·99	¼	¼	0 630·79	¼	¼	0 857·59
½		0 411·07	½	½	0 637·87	½	½	0 864·67
¾		0 418·16	¾	¾	0 644·96	¾	¾	0 871·76
15	...	0 425·25	23	1.7	0 652·05	31	1.15	0 878·85
¼		0 432·34	¼	¼	0 659·14	¼	¼	0 885·94
½		0 439·42	½	½	0 666·22	½	½	0 893·02
¾		0 446·51	¾	¾	0 673·31	¾	¾	0 900·11
16	1lb.	0 453·60	24	1.8	0 680·40	32	2 lb.	0 907·20

Ozs.	lbs. ozs.	kil. grams.	Ozs.	lbs. ozs.	kil. grams.	Ozs.	lbs.	kil. grams.
32¼	2. 0¼	0 914·29	34¼	2. 2¼	0 970·99	48	3	1 360·80
32½	0½	0 921·37	34½	2½	0 978·07	64	4	1 814·40
32¾	0¾	0 928·46	34¾	2¾	0 985·16	80	5	2 268·00
33	2. 1	0 935·55	35	2. 3	0 992·25	96	6	2 721·60
33¼	1¼	0 942·64	35¼	3¼	0 999·34	112	7	3 175·20
33½	1½	0 949·72	35½	3½	1 006·42	128	8	3 628·80
33¾	1¾	0 956·81	35¾	3¾	1 013·51	144	9	4 082·40
34	2. 2	0 963·90	36	2. 4	1 020·60	160	10	4 536·00

Ozs.	lbs. oz.	kilos. grams.	Ozs.	lbs. ozs.	kilos. grams.	Ozs.	lb. ozs.	kilos. grams.
33	2.1	0 935·5	65	4.1	1 842·7	97	6.1	2 749·9
34	2	0 963·9	66	2	1 871·1	98	2	2 778·3
35	3	0 992·2	67	3	1 899·4	99	3	2 806·6
36	4	1 020·6	68	4	1 927·8	100	4	2 835·0
37	5	1 048·9	69	5	1 956·1	101	5	2 863·3
38	6	1 077·3	70	6	1 984·5	102	6	2 891·7
39	7	1 105·6	71	7	2 012·8	103	7	2 920·0
40	8	1 134·0	72	8	2 041·2	104	8	2 948·4
41	9	1 162·3	73	9	2 069·5	105	9	2 976·7
42	10	1 190·7	74	10	2 097·9	106	10	3 005·1
43	11	1 219·0	75	11	2 126·2	107	11	3 033·4
44	12	1 247·4	76	12	2 154·6	108	12	3 061·8
45	13	1 275·7	77	13	2 182·9	109	13	3 090·1
46	14	1 304·1	78	14	2 211·3	110	14	3 118·5
47	15	1 332·4	79	15	2 239·6	111	15	3 146·8
48	3.0	1 360·8	80	5.0	2 268·0	112	7.0	3 175·2
49	1	1 389·1	81	1	2 296·3	113	1	3 203·5
50	2	1 417·5	82	2	2 324·7	114	2	3 231·9
51	3	1 445·8	83	3	2 353·0	115	3	3 260·2
52	4	1 474·2	84	4	2 381·4	116	4	3 288·6
53	5	1 502·5	85	5	2 409·7	117	5	3 316·9
54	6	1 530·9	86	6	2 438·1	118	6	3 345·3
55	7	1 559·2	87	7	2 466·4	119	7	3 373·6
56	8	1 587·6	88	8	2 494·8	120	8	3 402·0
57	9	1 615·9	89	9	2 523·1	121	9	3 430·3
58	10	1 644·3	90	10	2 551·5	122	10	3 458·7
59	11	1 672·6	91	11	2 579·8	123	11	3 487·0
60	12	1 701·0	92	12	2 608·2	124	12	3 515·4
61	13	1 729·3	93	13	2 636·5	125	13	3 543·7
62	14	1 757·7	94	14	2 664·9	126	14	3 572·1
63	15	1 786·0	95	15	2 693·2	127	15	3 600·4
64	4.0	1 814·4	96	6.0	2 721·6	128	8.0	3 628·8

Drm	=Ozs.	kil. grams.	Drms.	=Ozs.	kil. grams.	Ozs.	grams.	Ozs.	grams.
1	$\frac{1}{16}$	0 1·8	9	$\frac{9}{16}$	0 16·0	1	28·4	9	255·2
2	$\frac{1}{8}$	0 3·5	10	$\frac{5}{8}$	0 17·7	2	56·7	10	283·5
3	$\frac{3}{16}$	0 5·3	11	$\frac{11}{16}$	0 19·5	3	85·1	11	311·9
4	$\frac{1}{4}$	0 7·1	12	$\frac{3}{4}$	0 21·3	4	113·4	12	340·2
5	$\frac{5}{16}$	0 8·9	13	$\frac{13}{16}$	0 23·0	5	141·8	13	368·6
6	$\frac{3}{8}$	0 10·6	14	$\frac{7}{8}$	0 24·8	6	170·1	14	396·9
7	$\frac{7}{16}$	0 12·4	15	$\frac{15}{16}$	0 26·6	7	198·5	15	425·3
8	$\frac{1}{2}$	0 14·2	16	1 oz	0 28·4	8	226·8	16	453·6

Ozs.	lbs. oz.	kilos.	grams.	Ozs.	lbs. ozs.	kilos.	grams.	Ozs.	lb. ozs.	kilos.	grams.
129	8. 1	3	657·1	161	10.1	4	564·3	193	12.1	5	471·5
130	2	3	685·5	162	2	4	592·7	194	2	5	499·9
131	3	3	713·8	163	3	4	621·0	195	3	5	528·2
132	4	3	742·2	164	4	4	649·4	196	4	5	556·6
133	5	3	770·5	165	5	4	677·7	197	5	5	584·9
134	6	3	798·9	166	6	4	706·1	198	6	5	613·3
135	7	3	827·2	167	7	4	734·4	199	7	5	641·6
136	8	3	855·6	168	8	4	762·8	200	8	5	670·0
137	9	3	883·9	169	9	4	791·1	201	9	5	698·3
138	10	3	912·3	170	10	4	819·5	202	10	5	726·7
139	11	3	940·6	171	11	4	847·8	203	11	5	755·0
140	12	3	969·0	172	12	4	876·2	204	12	5	783·4
141	13	3	997·3	173	13	4	904·5	205	13	5	811·7
142	14	4	025·7	174	14	4	932·9	206	14	5	840·1
143	15	4	054·0	175	15	4	961·2	207	15	5	868·4
144	9.0	4	082·4	176	11.0	4	989·6	208	13.0	5	896·8
145	1	4	110·7	177	1	5	017·9	209	1	5	925·1
146	2	4	139·1	178	2	5	046·3	210	2	5	953·5
147	3	4	167·4	179	3	5	074·6	211	3	5	981·8
148	4	4	195·8	180	4	5	103·0	212	4	6	010·2
149	5	4	224·1	181	5	5	131·3	213	5	6	038·5
150	6	4	252·5	182	6	5	159·7	214	6	6	066·9
151	7	4	280·8	183	7	5	188·0	215	7	6	095·2
152	8	4	309·2	184	8	5	216·4	216	8	6	123·6
153	9	4	337·5	185	9	5	244·7	217	9	6	151·9
154	10	4	365·9	186	10	5	273·1	218	10	6	180·3
155	11	4	394·2	187	11	5	301·4	219	11	6	208·6
156	12	4	422·6	188	12	5	329·8	220	12	6	237·0
157	13	4	450·9	189	13	5	358·1	221	13	6	265·3
158	14	4	479·3	190	14	5	386·5	222	14	6	293·7
159	15	4	507·6	191	15	5	414·8	223	15	6	322·0
160	10.0	4	536·0	192	12 0	5	443·2	224	14.0	6	350·4

Ozs.	lbs.	kil.	grams.	Ozs.	lbs.	kil.	grams.	Ozs.	lbs.	kil.	grams.
232	14½	6	577·2	296	18½	8	391·6	360	22½	10	206·0
240	15	6	804·0	304	19	8	618·4	368	23	10	432·8
248	15½	7	030·8	312	19½	8	845·2	376	23½	10	659·6
256	16	7	257·6	320	20	9	072·0	384	24	10	886·4
264	16½	7	484·4	328	20½	9	298·8	400	25	11	340·0
272	17	7	711·2	336	21	9	525·6	416	26	11	793·6
280	17½	7	938·0	344	21½	9	752·4	432	27	12	247·2
288	18	8	164·8	352	22	9	979·2	448	28	12	700·8

CWTS., QRS., STONES, LBS. — KILOS. (1016 kg.)

cwt.	qr.	lb.	lbs.	kilos.	grams.	stns.	cwt.	qr.	lb.	lbs.	kilos.	grams.	st.
0	0	7	7	=3	175	...	2	1	0	252	114	300	18
0	0	14	14	6	350	1	2	1	7	59	117	475	...
0	0	21	21	9	525	...	2	1	14	66	120	650	19
0	1	0	28	12	700	2	2	1	21	73	123	825	...
0	1	7	35	15	875	...	2	2	0	80	127	000	20
0	1	14	42	19	050	3	2	2	7	87	130	175	...
0	1	21	49	22	225	...	2	2	14	94	133	350	21
0	1	22	50	22	679	...	2	2	20	300	136	071	...
0	2	0	56	25	400	4	2	2	21	301	136	525	...
0	2	7	63	28	575	...	2	3	0	08	139	700	22
0	2	14	70	31	750	5	2	3	7	15	142	875	...
0	2	21	77	34	925	...	2	3	14	22	146	050	23
0	3	0	84	38	100	6	2	3	21	29	149	225	...
0	3	7	91	41	275	...	3	0	0	36	152	400	24
0	3	14	98	44	450	7	3	0	7	43	155	575	...
0	3	16	100	45	357	...	3	0	14	350	158	750	25
0	3	21	105	47	625	...	3	0	21	57	161	925	...
1	0	0	12	50	800	8	3	1	0	64	165	100	26
1	0	7	19	53	975	...	3	1	7	71	168	275	...
1	0	14	26	57	150	9	3	1	14	78	171	450	27
1	0	21	33	60	325	...	3	1	21	85	174	625	...
1	1	0	40	63	500	10	3	2	0	92	177	800	28
1	1	7	47	66	675	...	3	2	7	99	180	975	...
1	1	10	150	68	036	...	3	2	8	400	181	429	...
1	1	14	54	69	850	11	3	2	14	406	184	150	29
1	1	21	61	73	025	...	3	2	21	13	187	325	...
1	2	0	68	76	200	12	3	3	0	20	190	500	30
1	2	7	75	79	375	...	3	3	7	27	193	675	...
1	2	14	82	82	550	13	3	3	14	34	196	850	31
1	2	21	89	85	725	...	3	3	21	41	200	025	...
1	3	0	96	88	900	14	4	0	0	48	203	200	32
1	3	4	200	90	714	...	4	0	2	450	204	107	...
1	3	7	203	92	075	...	4	0	7	55	206	375	...
1	3	14	10	95	250	15	4	0	14	62	209	550	33
1	3	21	17	98	425	...	4	0	21	69	212	725	...
2	0	0	24	101	600	16	4	1	0	76	215	900	34
2	0	7	31	104	775	...	4	1	7	83	219	075	...
2	0	14	38	107	950	17	4	1	14	90	222	250	35
2	0	21	45	111	125	...	4	1	21	97	225	425	...
2	0	26	250	113	393	...	4	1	24	500	226	786	...

cwt.	qr.	lb.	lbs.	kilos.	grams.	Tons	tnns.	kilos.	gms.	Tons	tnns.	kilos.	gms.
4	2	0	504	228	600	1	1	016	047	51	51	818	397
4	2	7	11	231	775	2	2	032	094	52	52	834	444
4	2	14	18	234	950	3	3	048	141	53	53	850	491
4	2	21	25	238	125	4	4	064	188	54	54	866	538
4	3	0	32	241	300	5	5	080	235	55	55	882	585
4	3	7	39	244	475	6	6	096	282	56	56	898	632
4	3	14	46	247	650	7	7	112	329	57	57	914	679
4	3	18	550	249	464	8	8	128	376	58	58	930	726
4	3	21	53	250	825	9	9	144	423	59	59	946	773
4	3	21	53	250	825	10	10	160	470	60	60	962	820
5	0	0	60	254	000	11	11	176	517	61	61	978	867
5	0	7	67	257	175	12	12	192	564	62	62	994	914
5	0	14	74	260	350	13	13	208	611	63	64	010	961
5	0	21	81	263	525	14	14	224	658	64	65	027	008
5	1	0	88	266	700	15	15	240	705	65	66	043	055
5	1	7	95	269	875	16	16	256	752	66	67	059	102
5	1	12	600	272	143	17	17	272	799	67	68	075	149
5	1	14	602	273	050	18	18	288	846	68	69	091	196
5	1	21	09	276	225	19	19	304	893	69	70	107	243
5	2	0	16	279	400	20	20	320	940	70	71	123	290
5	2	7	23	282	575	21	21	336	987	71	72	139	337
5	2	14	30	285	750	22	22	353	034	72	73	155	384
5	2	21	37	288	925	23	23	369	081	73	74	171	431
5	3	0	44	292	100	24	24	385	128	74	75	187	478
5	3	6	650	294	821	25	25	401	175	75	76	203	525
5	3	7	51	295	275	26	26	417	222	76	77	219	572
5	3	14	58	298	450	27	27	433	269	77	78	235	619
5	3	21	65	301	625	28	28	449	316	78	79	251	666
6	0	0	72	304	800	29	29	465	363	79	80	267	713
6	0	7	79	307	975	30	30	481	410	80	81	283	760
6	0	14	86	311	150	31	31	497	457	81	82	299	807
6	0	21	93	314	325	32	32	513	504	82	83	315	854
6	1	0	700	317	500	33	33	529	551	83	84	331	901
6	1	7	707	320	675	34	34	545	598	84	85	347	948
6	1	14	14	323	850	35	35	561	645	85	86	363	995
6	1	21	21	327	025	36	36	577	692	86	87	380	042
6	2	0	28	330	200	37	37	593	739	87	88	396	089
6	2	7	35	333	375	38	38	609	786	88	89	412	136
6	2	14	42	336	550	39	39	625	833	89	90	428	183
6	2	21	49	339	725	40	40	641	880	90	91	444	230
6	2	22	750	340	179	41	41	657	927	91	92	460	277
						42	42	673	974	92	93	476	324
						43	43	690	021	93	94	492	371
						44	44	706	068	94	95	508	418
						45	45	722	115	95	96	524	465
						46	46	738	162	96	97	540	512
						47	47	754	209	97	98	556	559
						48	48	770	256	98	99	572	606
						49	49	786	303	99	100	588	653
						50	50	802	350	100	101	604	700

48. TONS, CWTS., QRS., LBS. – TONNES & KILOS.

cwt.	qr.	lb.	lbs.	kilos.	grams.	cwt.	qr.	lb.	lbs.	kilos.	grams.
6	3	0	756	342	900	8	3	21	1001	454	025
6	3	7	63	346	075	9	0	0	08	457	200
6	3	14	70	349	250	9	0	7	15	460	375
6	3	21	77	352	425	9	0	14	22	463	550
7	0	0	84	355	600	9	0	21	29	466	725
7	0	7	91	358	775	9	1	0	36	469	900
7	0	14	98	361	950	9	1	7	43	473	075
7	0	16	800	362	857	9	1	14	1050	476	250
7	0	21	805	365	125	9	1	21	57	479	425
7	1	0	12	368	300	9	2	0	64	482	600
7	1	7	19	371	475	9	2	7	71	485	775
7	1	14	26	374	650	9	2	14	78	488	950
7	1	21	33	377	825	9	2	21	85	492	125
7	2	0	40	381	000	9	3	0	92	495	300
7	2	7	47	384	175	9	3	7	99	498	475
7	2	10	850	385	536	9	3	8	1100	498	929
7	2	14	54	387	350	9	3	14	1106	501	650
7	2	21	61	390	525	9	3	21	13	504	825
7	3	0	68	393	700	10	0	0	20	508	000
7	3	7	75	396	875	10	0	7	27	511	175
7	3	14	82	400	050	10	0	14	34	514	350
7	3	21	89	403	225	10	0	21	41	517	525
8	0	0	96	406	400	10	1	0	48	520	700
8	0	4	900	408	214	10	1	2	1150	521	607
8	0	7	903	409	575	10	1	7	55	523	875
8	0	14	10	412	750	10	1	14	62	527	050
8	0	21	17	415	925	10	1	21	69	530	225
8	1	0	24	419	100	10	2	0	76	533	400
8	1	7	31	422	275	10	2	7	83	536	575
8	1	14	38	425	450	10	2	14	90	539	750
8	1	21	45	428	625	10	2	21	97	542	925
8	1	26	950	430	893	10	2	24	1200	544	286
8	2	0	52	431	800	10	3	0	1204	546	100
8	2	7	59	434	975	10	3	7	11	549	275
8	2	14	66	438	150	10	3	14	18	552	450
8	2	21	73	441	325	10	3	21	25	555	625
8	3	0	80	444	500	11	0	0	32	558	800
8	3	7	87	447	675	11	0	7	39	561	975
8	3	14	94	450	850	11	0	14	46	565	150
8	3	20	1000	453	571	11	0	18	1250	566	964

cwt.	qr	lb.	lbs.	kiles.	grams.
11	0	21	1253	568	325
11	1	0	60	571	500
11	1	7	67	574	675
11	1	14	74	577	850
11	1	21	81	581	025
11	2	0	88	584	200
11	2	7	95	587	375
11	2	12	1300	589	643
11	2	14	1302	590	550
11	2	21	09	593	725
11	3	0	16	596	900
11	3	7	23	600	075
11	3	14	30	603	250
11	3	21	37	606	425
12	0	0	44	609	600
12	0	6	1350	612	321
12	0	7	51	612	775
12	0	14	58	615	950
12	0	21	65	619	125
12	1	0	72	622	300
12	1	7	79	625	475
12	1	14	86	628	650
12	1	21	93	631	825
12	2	0	1400	635	000
12	2	7	1407	638	175
12	2	14	14	641	350
12	2	21	21	644	525
12	3	0	28	647	700
12	3	7	35	650	875
12	3	14	42	654	050
12	3	21	49	657	225
12	3	22	1450	657	679
13	0	0	56	660	400
13	0	7	63	663	575
13	0	14	70	666	750
13	0	21	77	669	925
13	1	0	84	673	100
13	1	7	91	676	275
13	1	14	98	679	450
13	1	16	1500	680	357

Tons	tnns.	kilos.	gms.
1	1	016	047
2	2	032	094
3	3	048	141
4	4	064	188
5	5	080	235
6	6	096	282
7	7	112	329
8	8	128	376
9	9	144	423
10	10	160	470
11	11	176	517
12	12	192	564
13	13	208	611
14	14	224	658
15	15	240	705
16	16	256	752
17	17	272	799
18	18	288	846
19	19	304	893
20	20	320	940
21	21	336	987
22	22	353	034
23	23	369	081
24	24	385	128
25	25	401	175
26	26	417	222
27	27	433	269
28	28	449	316
29	29	465	363
30	30	481	410
31	31	497	457
32	32	513	504
33	33	529	551
34	34	545	598
35	35	561	645
36	36	577	692
37	37	593	739
38	38	609	786
39	39	625	833
40	40	641	880
41	41	657	927
42	42	673	974
43	43	690	021
44	44	706	068
45	45	722	115
46	46	738	162
47	47	754	209
48	48	770	256
49	49	786	303
50	50	802	350

Tons	tnns.	kilos.	gms.
51	51	818	397
52	52	834	444
53	53	850	491
54	54	866	538
55	55	882	585
56	56	898	632
57	57	914	679
58	58	930	726
59	59	946	773
60	60	962	820
61	61	978	867
62	62	994	914
63	64	010	961
64	65	027	008
65	66	043	055
66	67	059	102
67	68	075	149
68	69	091	196
69	70	107	243
70	71	123	290
71	72	139	337
72	73	155	384
73	74	171	431
74	75	187	478
75	76	203	525
76	77	219	572
77	78	235	619
78	79	251	666
79	80	267	713
80	81	283	760
81	82	299	807
82	83	315	854
83	84	331	901
84	85	347	948
85	86	363	995
86	87	380	042
87	88	396	089
88	89	412	136
89	90	428	183
90	91	444	230
91	92	460	277
92	93	476	324
93	94	492	371
94	95	508	418
95	96	524	465
96	97	540	512
97	98	556	559
98	99	572	606
99	100	588	653
100	101	604	700

60. TONS, CWTS., QRS., LBS. — TONNES & KILOS.

cwt.	qr.	lb.	lbs.	kilos.	grams.	cwt.	qr.	lb.	lbs.	kilos.	grams.
13	1	21	1505	682	625	15	2	21	1757	796	925
13	2	0	12	685	800	15	3	0	64	800	100
13	2	7	19	688	975	15	3	7	71	803	275
13	2	14	26	692	150	15	3	14	78	806	450
13	2	21	33	695	325	15	3	21	85	809	625
13	3	0	40	698	500	16	0	0	92	812	800
13	3	7	47	701	675	16	0	7	99	815	975
13	3	10	1550	703	036	16	0	8	1800	816	429
13	3	14	54	704	850	16	0	14	1806	819	150
13	3	21	61	708	025	16	0	21	13	822	325
14	0	0	68	711	200	16	1	0	20	825	500
14	0	7	75	714	375	16	1	7	27	828	675
14	0	14	82	717	550	16	1	14	34	831	850
14	0	21	89	720	725	16	1	21	41	835	025
14	1	0	96	723	900	16	2	0	48	838	200
14	1	4	1600	725	714	16	2	2	1850	839	107
14	1	7	1603	727	075	16	2	7	55	841	375
14	1	14	10	730	250	16	2	14	62	844	550
14	1	21	17	733	425	16	2	21	69	847	725
14	2	0	24	736	600	16	3	0	76	850	900
14	2	7	31	739	775	16	3	7	83	854	075
14	2	14	38	742	950	16	3	14	90	857	250
14	2	21	45	746	125	16	3	21	97	860	425
14	2	26	1650	748	393	16	3	24	1900	861	786
14	3	0	52	749	300	17	0	0	1904	863	600
14	3	7	59	752	475	17	0	7	11	866	775
14	3	14	66	755	650	17	0	14	18	869	950
14	3	21	73	758	825	17	0	21	25	873	125
15	0	0	80	762	000	17	1	0	32	876	300
15	0	7	87	765	175	17	1	7	39	879	475
15	0	14	94	768	350	17	1	14	46	882	650
15	0	20	1700	771	071	17	1	18	1950	884	464
15	0	21	1701	771	525	17	1	21	53	885	825
15	1	0	08	774	700	17	2	0	60	889	000
15	1	7	15	777	875	17	2	7	67	892	175
15	1	14	22	781	050	17	2	14	74	895	350
15	1	21	29	784	225	17	2	21	81	898	525
15	2	0	36	787	400	17	3	0	88	901	700
15	2	7	43	790	575	17	3	7	95	904	875
15	2	14	1750	793	750	17	3	12	2000	907	143

cwt.	qr.	lb.	lbs.	kilos.	grams.
17	3	14	2002	908	050
17	3	21	09	911	225
18	0	0	16	914	400
18	0	7	23	917	575
18	0	14	30	920	750
18	0	21	37	923	925
18	1	0	44	927	100
18	1	6	2050	929	821
18	1	7	51	930	275
18	1	14	58	933	450
18	1	21	65	936	625
18	2	0	72	939	800
18	2	7	79	942	975
18	2	14	86	946	150
18	2	21	93	949	325
18	3	0	2100	952	500
18	3	7	2107	955	675
18	3	14	14	958	850
18	3	21	21	962	025
19	0	0	28	965	200
19	0	7	35	968	375
19	0	14	42	971	550
19	0	21	49	974	725
19	0	22	2150	975	179
19	1	0	56	977	900
19	1	7	63	981	075
19	1	14	70	984	250
19	1	21	77	987	425
19	2	0	84	990	600
19	2	7	91	993	775
19	2	14	98	996	950
19	2	16	2200	997	857
19	2	21	2205	1000	125
19	3	0	12	1003	300
19	3	7	19	1006	475
19	3	14	26	1009	650
19	3	21	33	1012	825
20	0	0	2240	1016	000
20	0	7	47	1019	175
20	0	10	2250	1020	536

Tons	tnns.	kilos.	gms.
1	1	016	047
2	2	032	094
3	3	048	141
4	4	064	188
5	5	080	235
6	6	096	282
7	7	112	329
8	8	128	376
9	9	144	423
10	10	160	470
11	11	176	517
12	12	192	564
13	13	208	611
14	14	224	658
15	15	240	705
16	16	256	752
17	17	272	799
18	18	288	846
19	19	304	893
20	20	320	940
21	21	336	987
22	22	353	034
23	23	369	081
24	24	385	128
25	25	401	175
26	26	417	222
27	27	433	269
28	28	449	316
29	29	465	363
30	30	481	410
31	31	497	457
32	32	513	504
33	33	529	551
34	34	545	598
35	35	561	645
36	36	577	692
37	37	593	739
38	38	609	786
39	39	625	833
40	40	641	880
41	41	657	927
42	42	673	974
43	43	690	021
44	44	706	068
45	45	722	115
46	46	738	162
47	47	754	209
48	48	770	256
49	49	786	303
50	50	802	350

Tons	tnns.	kilos.	gms.
51	51	818	397
52	52	834	444
53	53	850	491
54	54	866	538
55	55	882	585
56	56	898	632
57	57	914	679
58	58	930	726
59	59	946	773
60	60	962	820
61	61	978	867
62	62	994	914
63	64	010	961
64	65	027	008
65	66	043	055
66	67	059	102
67	68	075	149
68	69	091	196
69	70	107	243
70	71	123	290
71	72	139	337
72	73	155	384
73	74	171	431
74	75	187	478
75	76	203	525
76	77	219	572
77	78	235	619
78	79	251	666
79	80	267	713
80	81	283	760
81	82	299	807
82	83	315	854
83	84	331	901
84	85	347	948
85	86	363	995
86	87	380	042
87	88	396	089
88	89	412	136
89	90	428	183
90	91	444	230
91	92	460	277
92	93	476	324
93	94	492	371
94	95	508	418
95	96	524	465
96	97	540	512
97	98	556	559
98	99	572	606
99	100	588	653
100	101	604	700

cwt.	qrs.	lbs.	lbs.	=kilos.	gms.	cwt.	qrs.	lbs.	lbs.	=kilos.	gms.
0	0	1	1	0	454	0	1	1	29	13	154
0	0	2	2	0	907	0	1	2	30	13	607
0	0	3	3	1	361	0	1	3	31	14	061
0	0	4	4	1	814	0	1	4	32	14	514
0	0	5	5	2	268	0	1	5	33	14	968
0	0	6	6	2	721	0	1	6	34	15	421
0	0	7	7	3	175	0	1	7	35	15	875
0	0	8	8	3	629	0	1	8	36	16	329
0	0	9	9	4	082	0	1	9	37	16	782
0	0	10	10	4	536	0	1	10	38	17	236
0	0	11	11	4	989	0	1	11	39	17	689
0	0	12	*Stones.* 12	5	443	0	1	12	*Stones.* 40	18	143
0	0	13	13	5	896	0	1	13	41	18	596
0	0	14	¹14	6	350	0	1	14	³42	19	050
0	0	15	15	6	804	0	1	15	43	19	504
0	0	16	16	7	257	0	1	16	44	19	957
0	0	17	17	7	711	0	1	17	45	20	411
0	0	18	18	8	164	0	1	18	46	20	864
0	0	19	19	8	618	0	1	19	47	21	318
0	0	20	20	9	071	0	1	20	48	21	771
0	0	21	21	9	525	0	1	21	49	22	225
0	0	22	22	9	979	0	1	22	50	22	679
0	0	23	23	10	432	0	1	23	51	23	132
0	0	24	24	10	886	0	1	24	52	23	586
0	0	25	25	11	339	0	1	25	53	24	039
0	0	26	*Stones.* 26	11	793	0	1	26	*Stones.* 54	24	493
0	0	27	27	12	246	0	1	27	55	24	946
0	1	0	²28	12	700	0	2	0	⁴56	25	400

T.	c.	q.	lb.	lbs.	=kilos.	gms.	T.	c.	q.	lb.	lbs.	=kilos.	gms.
0	4	1	24	500	226	796	4	9	1	4	10,000	4,535	924
0	8	3	20	1000	453	592	4	18	0	24	11,000	4,989	517
0	13	1	16	1500	680	389	5	7	0	16	12,000	5,443	109
0	17	3	12	2000	907	185	5	16	0	8	13,000	5,896	701
1	6	3	4	3000	1,360	777	6	5	0	0	14,000	6,350	294
1	15	2	24	4000	1,814	370	6	13	3	20	15,000	6,803	886
2	4	2	16	5000	2,267	962	7	2	3	12	16,000	7,257	479
2	13	2	8	6000	2,721	554	7	11	3	4	17,000	7,711	071
3	2	2	0	7000	3,175	147	8	0	2	24	18,000	8,164	663
3	11	1	20	8000	3,628	739	8	9	2	16	19,000	8,618	256
4	0	1	12	9000	4,082	332	8	18	2	8	20,000	9,071	848

cwt.	qrs.	lbs.	lbs.	=kilos.	gms.	cwt.	qrs.	lbs.	lbs.	=kilos.	gms.
0	2	1	57	25	854	0	3	1	85	38	554
0	2	2	58	26	307	0	3	2	86	39	007
0	2	3	59	26	761	0	3	3	87	39	461
0	2	4	60	27	214	0	3	4	88	39	914
0	2	5	61	27	668	0	3	5	89	40	368
0	2	6	62	28	121	0	3	6	90	40	821
0	2	7	63	28	575	0	3	7	91	41	275
0	2	8	64	29	029	0	3	8	92	41	729
0	2	9	65	29	482	0	3	9	93	42	182
0	2	10	66	29	936	0	3	10	94	42	636
0	2	11	67	30	389	0	3	11	95	43	089
0	2	12	*Stones.* 68	30	843	0	3	12	*Stones.* 96	43	543
0	2	13	69	31	296	0	3	13	97	43	996
0	2	14	⁵70	31	750	0	3	14	⁷98	44	450
0	2	15	71	32	204	0	3	15	99	44	904
0	2	16	72	32	657	0	3	16	100	45	357
0	2	17	73	33	111	0	3	17	101	45	811
0	2	18	74	33	564	0	3	18	102	46	264
0	2	19	75	34	018	0	3	19	103	46	718
0	2	20	76	34	471	0	3	20	104	47	171
0	2	21	77	34	925	0	3	21	105	47	625
0	2	22	78	35	379	0	3	22	106	48	079
0	2	23	79	35	832	0	3	23	107	48	532
0	2	24	80	36	286	0	3	24	108	48	986
0	2	25	81	36	739	0	3	25	109	49	439
0	2	26	*Stones.* 82	37	193	0	3	26	*Stones.* 110	49	893
0	2	27	83	37	646	0	3	27	111	50	346
0	3	0	⁶84	38	100	1	0	0	⁸112	50	800

=lbs.	Tons	=kilos.	gms.	=lbs.	Tons	=kilos.	gms.
560	¼	254	012	12,320	5½	5,588	258
1,120	½	508	023	13,440	6	6,096	282
2,240	1	1,016	047	14,560	6½	6,604	305
3,360	1½	1,524	070	15,680	7	7,112	329
4,480	2	2,032	094	16,800	7½	7,620	352
5,600	2½	2,540	117	17,920	8	8,128	376
6,720	3	3,048	141	19,040	8½	8,636	399
7,840	3½	3,556	164	20,160	9	9,144	423
8,960	4	4,064	188	21,280	9½	9,652	446
10,080	4½	4,572	211	22,400	10	10,160	470
11,200	5	5,080	235	24,640	11	11,176	517

LBS. — TONS, CWTS., QRS., & KILOS.

cwt.	qrs.	lbs.	lbs.	=kilos.	gms.	cwt.	qrs.	lbs.	lbs.	=kilos.	gms.
1	0	1	113	51	254	1	1	1	141	63	954
1	0	2	114	51	707	1	1	2	142	64	407
1	0	3	115	52	161	1	1	3	143	64	861
1	0	4	116	52	614	1	1	4	144	65	314
1	0	5	117	53	068	1	1	5	145	65	768
1	0	6	118	53	521	1	1	6	146	66	221
1	0	7	119	53	975	1	1	7	147	66	675
1	0	8	120	54	429	1	1	8	148	67	129
1	0	9	121	54	882	1	1	9	149	67	582
1	0	10	122	55	336	1	1	10	150	68	036
1	0	11	123	55	789	1	1	11	151	68	489
1	0	12	*Stones.* 124	56	243	1	1	12	*Stones.* 152	68	943
1	0	13	125	56	696	1	1	13	153	69	396
1	0	14	⁹126	57	150	1	1	14	¹¹154	69	850
1	0	15	127	57	604	1	1	15	155	70	304
1	0	16	128	58	057	1	1	16	156	70	757
1	0	17	129	58	511	1	1	17	157	71	211
1	0	18	130	58	964	1	1	18	158	71	664
1	0	19	131	59	418	1	1	19	159	72	118
1	0	20	132	59	871	1	1	20	160	72	571
1	0	21	133	60	325	1	1	21	161	73	025
1	0	22	134	60	779	1	1	22	162	73	479
1	0	23	135	61	232	1	1	23	163	73	932
1	0	24	136	61	686	1	1	24	164	74	386
1	0	25	137	62	139	1	1	25	165	74	839
1	0	26	*Stones.* 138	62	593	1	1	26	*Stones.* 166	75	293
1	0	27	139	63	046	1	1	27	167	75	746
1	1	0	¹⁰140	63	500	1	2	0	¹²168	76	200

T.	c.	q.	lb.	lbs.	=kilos.	gms.	T.	c.	q.	lb.	lbs.	=kilos.	gms.
0	4	1	24	500	226	796	4	9	1	4	10,000	4,535	924
0	8	3	20	1000	453	592	4	18	0	24	11,000	4,989	517
0	13	1	16	1500	680	389	5	7	0	16	12,000	5,443	109
0	17	3	12	2000	907	185	5	16	0	8	13,000	5,896	701
1	6	3	4	3000	1,360	777	6	5	0	0	14,000	6,350	294
1	15	2	24	4000	1,814	370	6	13	3	20	15,000	6,803	886
2	4	2	16	5000	2,267	962	7	2	3	12	16,000	7,257	479
2	13	2	8	6000	2,721	554	7	11	3	4	17,000	7,711	071
3	2	2	0	7000	3,175	147	8	0	2	24	18,000	8,164	663
3	11	1	20	8000	3,628	739	8	9	2	16	19,000	8,618	256
4	0	1	12	9000	4,082	332	8	18	2	8	20,000	9,071	848

cwt.	qrs.	lbs.	lbs.	=kilos.	gms.	cwt.	qrs.	lbs.	lbs.	=kilos.	gms.
1	2	1	169	76	654	1	3	1	197	89	354
1	2	2	170	77	107	1	3	2	198	89	807
1	2	3	171	77	561	1	3	3	199	90	261
1	2	4	172	78	014	1	3	4	200	90	714
1	2	5	173	78	468	1	3	5	201	91	168
1	2	6	174	78	921	1	3	6	202	91	621
1	2	7	175	79	375	1	3	7	203	92	075
1	2	8	176	79	829	1	3	8	204	92	529
1	2	9	177	80	282	1	3	9	205	92	982
1	2	10	178	80	736	1	3	10	206	93	436
1	2	11	179	81	189	1	3	11	207	93	889
1	2	12	*Stones.* 180	81	643	1	3	12	*Stones.* 208	94	343
1	2	13	181	82	096	1	3	13	209	94	796
1	2	14	13 182	82	550	1	3	14	15 210	95	250
1	2	15	183	83	004	1	3	15	211	95	704
1	2	16	184	83	457	1	3	16	212	96	157
1	2	17	185	83	911	1	3	17	213	96	611
1	2	18	186	84	364	1	3	18	214	97	064
1	2	19	187	84	818	1	3	19	215	97	518
1	2	20	188	85	271	1	3	20	216	97	971
1	2	21	189	85	725	1	3	21	217	98	425
1	2	22	190	86	179	1	3	22	218	98	879
1	2	23	191	86	632	1	3	23	219	99	332
1	2	24	192	87	086	1	3	24	220	99	786
1	2	25	193	87	539	1	3	25	221	100	239
1	2	26	*Stones.* 194	87	993	1	3	26	*Stones.* 222	100	693
1	2	27	195	88	446	1	3	27	223	101	146
1	3	0	14 196	88	900	2	0	0	16 224	101	600

=lbs.	Tons	=kilos.	gms.	=lbs.	Tons	=kilos.	gms.
560	¼	254	012	12,320	5½	5,588	258
1,120	½	508	023	13,440	6	6,096	282
2,240	1	1,016	047	14,560	6½	6,604	305
3,360	1½	1,524	070	15,680	7	7,112	329
4,480	2	2,032	094	16,800	7½	7,620	352
5,600	2½	2,540	117	17,920	8	8,128	376
6,720	3	3,048	141	19,040	8½	8,636	399
7,840	3½	3,556	164	20,160	9	9,144	423
8,960	4	4,064	188	21,280	9½	9,652	446
10,080	4½	4,572	211	22,400	10	10,160	470
11,200	5	5,080	235	24,640	11	11,176	517

LBS. — TONS, CWTS., QRS., & KILOS.

cwt.	qrs.	lbs.	lbs.	=kilos.	gms.	cwt.	qrs.	lbs.	lbs.	=kilos.	gms.
2	0	1	225	102	054	2	1	1	253	114	754
2	0	2	226	102	507	2	1	2	254	115	207
2	0	3	227	102	961	2	1	3	255	115	661
2	0	4	228	103	414	2	1	4	256	116	114
2	0	5	229	103	868	2	1	5	257	116	568
2	0	6	230	104	321	2	1	6	258	117	021
2	0	7	**231**	104	775	2	1	7	**259**	117	475
2	0	8	232	105	229	2	1	8	260	117	929
2	0	9	233	105	682	2	1	9	261	118	382
2	0	10	234	106	136	2	1	10	262	118	836
2	0	11	235	106	589	2	1	11	263	119	289
2	0	12	*Stones.* 236	107	043	2	1	12	264	119	743
2	0	13	237	107	496	2	1	13	*Stones.* 265	120	196
2	0	14	[17]**238**	107	950	2	1	14	[19]**266**	120	650
2	0	15	239	108	404	2	1	15	267	121	104
2	0	16	240	108	857	2	1	16	268	121	557
2	0	17	241	109	311	2	1	17	269	122	011
2	0	18	242	109	764	2	1	18	270	122	464
2	0	19	243	110	218	2	1	19	271	122	918
2	0	20	244	110	671	2	1	20	272	123	371
2	0	21	**245**	111	125	2	1	21	**273**	123	825
2	0	22	246	111	579	2	1	22	274	124	279
2	0	23	247	112	032	2	1	23	275	124	732
2	0	24	248	112	486	2	1	24	276	125	186
2	0	25	249	112	939	2	1	25	277	125	639
2	0	26	*Stones.* 250	113	393	2	1	26	278	126	093
2	0	27	251	113	846	2	1	27	*Stones.* 279	126	546
2	1	0	[18]**252**	114	300	2	2	0	[20]**280**	127	000

T.	c.	q.	lb.	lbs.	=kilos.	gms.	T.	c.	q.	lb.	lbs.	=kilos.	gms.
0	4	1	24	500	226	796	4	9	1	4	10,000	4,535	924
0	8	3	20	1000	453	592	4	18	0	24	11,000	4,989	517
0	13	1	16	1500	680	389	5	7	0	16	12,000	5,443	109
0	17	3	12	2000	907	185	5	16	0	8	13,000	5,896	701
1	6	3	4	3000	1,360	777	6	5	0	0	14,000	6,350	294
1	15	2	24	4000	1,814	370	6	13	3	20	15,000	6,803	886
2	4	2	16	5000	2,267	962	7	2	3	12	16,000	7,257	479
2	13	2	8	6000	2,721	554	7	11	3	4	17,000	7,711	071
3	2	2	0	7000	3,175	147	8	0	2	24	18,000	8,164	663
3	11	1	20	8000	3,628	739	8	9	2	16	19,000	8,618	256
4	0	1	12	9000	4,082	332	8	18	2	8	20,000	9,071	848

cwt.	qrs.	lbs.	lbs.	=kilos.	gms.	cwt.	qrs.	lbs.	lbs.	=kilos.	gms.
2	2	1	281	127	454	2	3	1	309	140	154
2	2	2	282	127	907	2	3	2	310	140	607
2	2	3	283	128	361	2	3	3	311	141	061
2	2	4	284	128	814	2	3	4	312	141	514
2	2	5	285	129	268	2	3	5	313	141	968
2	2	6	286	129	721	2	3	6	314	142	421
2	2	7	287	130	175	2	3	7	315	142	875
2	2	8	288	130	629	2	3	8	316	143	329
2	2	9	289	131	082	2	3	9	317	143	782
2	2	10	290	131	536	2	3	10	318	144	236
2	2	11	291	131	989	2	3	11	319	144	689
2	2	12	*Stones.* 292	132	443	2	3	12	*Stones.* 320	145	143
2	2	13	293	132	896	2	3	13	321	145	596
2	2	14	21 294	133	350	2	3	14	23 322	146	050
2	2	15	295	133	804	2	3	15	323	146	504
2	2	16	296	134	257	2	3	16	324	146	957
2	2	17	297	134	711	2	3	17	325	147	411
2	2	18	298	135	164	2	3	18	326	147	864
2	2	19	299	135	618	2	3	19	327	148	318
2	2	20	300	136	071	2	3	20	328	148	771
2	2	21	301	136	525	2	3	21	329	149	225
2	2	22	302	136	979	2	3	22	330	149	679
2	2	23	303	137	432	2	3	23	331	150	132
2	2	24	304	137	886	2	3	24	332	150	586
2	2	25	305	138	339	2	3	25	333	151	039
2	2	26	*Stones.* 306	138	793	2	3	26	*Stones.* 334	151	493
2	2	27	307	139	246	2	3	27	335	151	946
2	3	0	23 308	139	700	3	0	0	24 336	152	400

=lbs.	Tons	=kilos.	gms.	=lbs.	Tons	=kilos.	gms.
560	¼	254	012	12,320	5½	5,588	258
1,120	½	508	023	13,440	6	6,096	282
2,240	1	1,016	047	14,560	6½	6,604	305
3,360	1½	1,524	070	15,680	7	7,112	329
4,480	2	2,032	094	16,800	7½	7,620	352
5,600	2½	2,540	117	17,920	8	8,128	376
6,720	3	3,048	141	19,040	8½	8,636	399
7,840	3½	3,556	164	20,160	9	9,144	423
8,960	4	4,064	188	21,280	9½	9,652	446
10,080	4½	4,572	211	22,400	10	10,160	470
11,200	5	5,080	235	24,640	11	11,176	517

E

LBS. – TONS, CWTS., QRS., & KILOS.

cwt.	qrs.	lbs.	lbs.	=kilos.	gms.	cwt.	qrs.	lbs.	lbs.	=kilos.	gms.
3	0	1	337	152	854	3	1	1	365	165	554
3	0	2	338	153	307	3	1	2	366	166	007
3	0	3	339	153	761	3	1	3	367	166	461
3	0	4	340	154	214	3	1	4	368	166	914
3	0	5	341	154	668	3	1	5	369	167	368
3	0	6	342	155	121	3	1	6	370	167	821
3	0	7	343	155	575	3	1	7	371	168	275
3	0	8	344	156	029	3	1	8	372	168	729
3	0	9	345	156	482	3	1	9	373	169	182
3	0	10	346	156	936	3	1	10	374	169	636
3	0	11	347	157	389	3	1	11	375	170	089
3	0	12	*Stones.* 348	157	843	3	1	12	*Stones.* 376	170	543
3	0	13	349	158	296	3	1	13	377	170	996
3	0	14	25 350	158	750	3	1	14	27 378	171	450
3	0	15	351	159	204	3	1	15	379	171	904
3	0	16	352	159	657	3	1	16	380	172	357
3	0	17	353	160	111	3	1	17	381	172	811
3	0	18	354	160	564	3	1	18	382	173	264
3	0	19	355	161	018	3	1	19	383	173	718
3	0	20	356	161	471	3	1	20	384	174	171
3	0	21	357	161	925	3	1	21	385	174	625
3	0	22	358	162	379	3	1	22	386	175	079
3	0	23	359	162	832	3	1	23	387	175	532
3	0	24	360	163	286	3	1	24	388	175	986
3	0	25	361	163	739	3	1	25	389	176	439
3	0	26	*Stones.* 362	164	193	3	1	26	*Stones.* 390	176	893
3	0	27	363	164	646	3	1	27	391	177	346
3	1	0	26 364	165	100	3	2	0	28 392	177	800

T.	c.	q.	lb.	lbs.	=kilos.	gms.	T.	c.	q.	lb.	lbs.	=kilos.	gms.
0	4	1	24	500	226	796	4	9	1	4	10,000	4,535	92
0	8	3	20	1000	453	592	4	18	0	24	11,000	4,989	51
0	13	1	16	1500	680	389	5	7	0	16	12,000	5,443	10
0	17	3	12	2000	907	185	5	16	0	8	13,000	5,896	70
1	6	3	4	3000	1,360	777	6	5	0	0	14,000	6,350	29
1	15	2	24	4000	1,814	370	6	13	3	20	15,000	6,803	88
2	4	2	16	5000	2,267	962	7	2	3	12	16,000	7,257	47
2	13	2	8	6000	2,721	554	7	11	3	4	17,000	7,711	07
3	2	2	0	7000	3,175	147	8	0	2	24	18,000	8,164	66
3	11	1	20	8000	3,628	739	8	9	2	16	19,000	8,618	25
4	0	1	12	9000	4,082	332	8	18	2	8	20,000	9,071	84

cwt.	qrs.	lbs.	lbs.	=kilos.	gms.	cwt.	qrs.	lbs.	lbs.	=kilos.	gms.
3	2	1	393	178	254	3	3	1	421	190	954
3	2	2	394	178	707	3	3	2	422	191	407
3	2	3	395	179	161	3	3	3	423	191	861
3	2	4	396	179	614	3	3	4	424	192	314
3	2	5	397	180	068	3	3	5	425	192	768
3	2	6	398	180	521	3	3	6	426	193	221
3	2	7	399	180	975	3	3	7	427	193	675
3	2	8	400	181	429	3	3	8	428	194	129
3	2	9	401	181	882	3	3	9	429	194	582
3	2	10	402	182	336	3	3	10	430	195	036
3	2	11	403	182	789	3	3	11	431	195	489
3	2	12	404	183	243	3	3	12	432	195	943
3	2	13	405	183	696	3	3	13	433	196	396
3	2	14	29 406	184	150	3	3	14	31 434	196	850
3	2	15	407	184	604	3	3	15	435	197	304
3	2	16	408	185	057	3	3	16	436	197	757
3	2	17	409	185	511	3	3	17	437	198	211
3	2	18	410	185	964	3	3	18	438	198	664
3	2	19	411	186	418	3	3	19	439	199	118
3	2	20	412	186	871	3	3	20	440	199	571
3	2	21	413	187	325	3	3	21	441	200	025
3	2	22	414	187	779	3	3	22	442	200	479
3	2	23	415	188	232	3	3	23	443	200	932
3	2	24	416	188	686	3	3	24	444	201	386
3	2	25	417	189	139	3	3	25	445	201	839
3	2	26	418	189	593	3	3	26	446	202	293
3	2	27	419	190	046	3	3	27	447	202	746
3	3	0	30 420	190	500	4	0	0	32 448	203	200

=lbs.	Tons	=kilos.	gms.	=lbs.	Tons	=kilos.	gms.
560	¼	254	012	12,320	5½	5,588	258
1,120	½	508	023	13,440	6	6,096	282
2,240	1	1,016	047	14,560	6½	6,604	305
3,360	1½	1,524	070	15,680	7	7,112	329
4,480	2	2,032	094	16,800	7½	7,620	352
5,600	2½	2,540	117	17,920	8	8,128	376
6,720	3	3,048	141	19,040	8½	8,636	399
7,840	3½	3,556	164	20,160	9	9,144	423
8,960	4	4,064	188	21,280	9½	9,652	446
10,080	4½	4,572	211	22,400	10	10,160	470
11,200	5	5,080	235	24.640	11	11,176	517

cwt.	qrs.	lbs.	lbs.	=kilos.	gms.	cwt.	qrs.	lbs.	lbs.	=kilos.	gms.
4	0	1	449	203	654	4	1	1	477	216	354
4	0	2	450	204	107	4	1	2	478	216	807
4	0	3	451	204	561	4	1	3	479	217	261
4	0	4	452	205	014	4	1	4	480	217	714
4	0	5	453	205	468	4	1	5	481	218	168
4	0	6	454	205	921	4	1	6	482	218	621
4	0	7	**455**	206	375	4	1	7	**483**	219	075
4	0	8	456	206	829	4	1	8	484	219	529
4	0	9	457	207	282	4	1	9	485	219	982
4	0	10	458	207	736	4	1	10	486	220	436
4	0	11	459	208	189	4	1	11	487	220	889
4	0	12	*Stones.* 460	208	643	4	1	12	*Stones.* 488	221	343
4	0	13	461	209	096	4	1	13	489	221	796
4	0	14	33 **462**	209	550	4	1	14	35 **490**	222	250
4	0	15	463	210	004	4	1	15	491	222	704
4	0	16	464	210	457	4	1	16	492	223	157
4	0	17	465	210	911	4	1	17	493	223	611
4	0	18	466	211	364	4	1	18	494	224	064
4	0	19	467	211	818	4	1	19	495	224	518
4	0	20	468	212	271	4	1	20	496	224	971
4	0	21	**469**	212	725	4	1	21	**497**	225	425
4	0	22	470	213	179	4	1	22	498	225	879
4	0	23	471	213	632	4	1	23	499	226	332
4	0	24	472	214	086	4	1	24	500	226	786
4	0	25	473	214	539	4	1	25	501	227	239
4	0	26	*Stones.* 474	214	993	4	1	26	*Stones.* 502	227	693
4	0	27	475	215	446	4	1	27	503	228	146
4	1	0	34 **476**	215	900	4	2	0	36 **504**	228	600

T.	c.	q.	lb.	lbs.	=kilos.	gms.	T.	c.	q.	lb.	lbs.	=kilos.	gms.
0	4	1	24	500	226	796	4	9	1	4	10,000	4,535	924
0	8	3	20	1000	453	592	4	18	0	24	11,000	4,989	517
0	13	1	16	1500	680	389	5	7	0	16	12,000	5,443	109
0	17	3	12	2000	907	185	5	16	0	8	13,000	5,896	701
1	6	3	4	3000	1,360	777	6	5	0	0	14,000	6,350	294
1	15	2	24	4000	1,814	370	6	13	3	20	15,000	6,803	886
2	4	2	16	5000	2,267	962	7	2	3	12	16,000	7,257	479
2	13	2	8	6000	2,721	554	7	11	3	4	17,000	7,711	071
3	2	2	0	7000	3,175	147	8	0	2	24	18,000	8,164	663
3	11	1	20	8000	3,628	739	8	9	2	16	19,000	8,618	256
4	0	1	12	9000	4,082	332	8	18	2	8	20,000	9,071	848

cwt.	qrs.	lbs.	lbs.	=kilos.	gms.	cwt.	qrs.	lbs.	lbs.	=kilos.	gms.
4	2	1	505	229	054	4	3	1	533	241	754
4	2	2	506	229	507	4	3	2	534	242	207
4	2	3	507	229	961	4	3	3	535	242	661
4	2	4	508	230	414	4	3	4	536	243	114
4	2	5	509	230	868	4	3	5	537	243	568
4	2	6	510	231	321	4	3	6	538	244	021
4	2	7	511	231	775	4	3	7	539	244	475
4	2	8	512	232	229	4	3	8	540	244	929
4	2	9	513	232	682	4	3	9	541	245	382
4	2	10	514	233	136	4	3	10	542	245	836
4	2	11	515	233	589	4	3	11	543	246	289
4	2	12	*Stones.* 516	234	043	4	3	12	*Stones.* 544	246	743
4	2	13	517	234	496	4	3	13	545	247	196
4	2	14	37 518	234	950	4	3	14	39 546	247	650
4	2	15	519	235	404	4	3	15	547	248	104
4	2	16	520	235	857	4	3	16	548	248	557
4	2	17	521	236	311	4	3	17	549	249	011
4	2	18	522	236	764	4	3	18	550	249	464
4	2	19	523	237	218	4	3	19	551	249	918
4	2	20	524	237	671	4	3	20	552	250	371
4	2	21	525	238	125	4	3	21	553	250	825
4	2	22	526	238	579	4	3	22	554	251	279
4	2	23	527	239	032	4	3	23	555	251	732
4	2	24	528	239	486	4	3	24	556	252	186
4	2	25	529	239	939	4	3	25	557	252	639
4	2	26	*Stones.* 530	240	393	4	3	26	*Stones.* 558	253	093
4	2	27	38 531	240	846	4	3	27	559	253	546
4	3	0	38 532	241	300	5	0	0	40 560	254	000

=lbs.	Tons	=kilos.	gms.	=lbs.	Tons	=kilos.	gms.
560	¼	254	012	12,320	5½	5,588	258
1,120	½	508	023	13,440	6	6,096	282
2,240	1	1,016	047	14,560	6½	6,604	305
3,360	1½	1,524	070	15,680	7	7,112	329
4,480	2	2,032	094	16,800	7½	7,620	352
5,600	2½	2,540	117	17,920	8	8,128	376
6,720	3	3,048	141	19,040	8½	8,636	399
7,840	3½	3,556	164	20,160	9	9,144	423
8,960	4	4,064	188	21,280	9½	9,652	446
10,080	4½	4,572	211	22,400	10	10,160	470
11,200	5	5,080	235	24,640	11	11,176	517

LBS. = TONS, CWTS., QRS., & KILOS.

cwt.	qrs.	lbs.	lbs.	=kilos.	gms.	cwt.	qrs.	lbs.	lbs.	=kilos.	gms.
5	0	1	561	254	454	5	1	1	589	267	154
5	0	2	562	254	907	5	1	2	590	267	607
5	0	3	563	255	361	5	1	3	591	268	061
5	0	4	564	255	814	5	1	4	592	268	514
5	0	5	565	256	268	5	1	5	593	268	968
5	0	6	566	256	721	5	1	6	594	269	421
5	0	7	567	257	175	5	1	7	595	269	875
5	0	8	568	257	629	5	1	8	596	270	329
5	0	9	569	258	082	5	1	9	597	270	782
5	0	10	570	258	536	5	1	10	598	271	236
5	0	11	571	258	989	5	1	11	599	271	689
5	0	12	572 *Stones.*	259	443	5	1	12	600 *Stones.*	272	143
5	0	13	573	259	896	5	1	13	601	272	596
5	0	14	41 574	260	350	5	1	14	43 602	273	050
5	0	15	575	260	804	5	1	15	603	273	504
5	0	16	576	261	257	5	1	16	604	273	957
5	0	17	577	261	711	5	1	17	605	274	411
5	0	18	578	262	164	5	1	18	606	274	864
5	0	19	579	262	618	5	1	19	607	275	318
5	0	20	580	263	071	5	1	20	608	275	771
5	0	21	581	263	525	5	1	21	609	276	225
5	0	22	582	263	979	5	1	22	610	276	679
5	0	23	583	264	432	5	1	23	611	277	132
5	0	24	584	264	886	5	1	24	612	277	586
5	0	25	585	265	339	5	1	25	613	278	039
5	0	26	586	265	793	5	1	26	614	278	493
5	0	27	587 *Stones.*	266	246	5	1	27	615 *Stones.*	278	946
5	1	0	42 588	266	700	5	2	0	44 616	279	400

T.	c.	q.	lb.	lbs.	=kilos.	gms.	T.	c.	q.	lb.	lbs.	=kilos.	gms.
0	4	1	24	500	226	796	4	9	1	4	10,000	4,535	924
0	8	3	20	1000	453	592	4	18	0	24	11,000	4,989	517
0	13	1	16	1500	680	389	5	7	0	16	12,000	5,443	109
0	17	3	12	2000	907	185	5	16	0	8	13,000	5,896	701
1	6	3	4	3000	1,360	777	6	5	0	0	14,000	6,350	294
1	15	2	24	4000	1,814	370	6	13	3	20	15,000	6,803	886
2	4	2	16	5000	2,267	962	7	2	3	12	16,000	7,257	479
2	13	2	8	6000	2,721	554	7	11	3	4	17,000	7,711	071
3	2	2	0	7000	3,175	147	8	0	2	24	18,000	8,164	663
3	11	1	20	8000	3,628	739	8	9	2	16	19,000	8,618	256
4	0	1	12	9000	4,082	332	8	18	2	8	20,000	9,071	848

cwt.	qrs.	lbs.	lbs.	=kilos.	gms.	cwt.	qrs.	lbs.	lbs.	=kilos.	gms.
5	2	1	617	279	854	5	3	1	645	292	554
5	2	2	618	280	307	5	3	2	646	293	007
5	2	3	619	280	761	5	3	3	647	293	461
5	2	4	620	281	214	5	3	4	648	293	914
5	2	5	621	281	668	5	3	5	649	294	368
5	2	6	622	282	121	5	3	6	650	294	821
5	2	7	**623**	282	575	5	3	7	**651**	295	275
5	2	8	624	283	029	5	3	8	652	295	729
5	2	9	625	283	482	5	3	9	653	296	182
5	2	10	626	283	936	5	3	10	654	296	636
5	2	11	627	284	389	5	3	11	655	297	089
5	2	12	628	284	843	5	3	12	656	297	543
5	2	13	629	285	296	5	3	13	657	297	996
5	2	14	45 **630**	285	750	5	3	14	47 **658**	298	450
5	2	15	631	286	204	5	3	15	659	298	904
5	2	16	632	286	657	5	3	16	660	299	357
5	2	17	633	287	111	5	3	17	661	299	811
5	2	18	634	287	564	5	3	18	662	300	264
5	2	19	635	288	018	5	3	19	663	300	718
5	2	20	636	288	471	5	3	20	664	301	171
5	2	21	**637**	288	925	5	3	21	**665**	301	625
5	2	22	638	289	379	5	3	22	666	302	079
5	2	23	639	289	832	5	3	23	667	302	532
5	2	24	640	290	286	5	3	24	668	302	986
5	2	25	641	290	739	5	3	25	669	303	439
5	2	26	642	291	193	5	3	26	670	303	893
5	2	27	643	291	646	5	3	27	671	304	346
5	3	0	46 **644**	292	100	6	0	0	48 **672**	304	800

=lbs.	Tons	=kilos.	gms.	=lbs.	Tons	=kilos.	gms.
560	¼	254	012	12,320	5½	5,588	258
1,120	½	508	023	13,440	6	6,096	282
2,240	1	1,016	047	14,560	6½	6,604	305
3,360	1½	1,524	070	15,680	7	7,112	329
4,480	2	2,032	094	16,800	7½	7,620	352
5,600	2½	2,540	117	17,920	8	8,128	376
6,720	3	3,048	141	19,040	8½	8,636	399
7,840	3½	3,556	164	20,160	9	9,144	423
8,960	4	4,064	188	21,280	9½	9,652	446
10,080	4½	4,572	211	22,400	10	10,160	470
11,200	5	5,080	235	24,640	11	11,176	517

cwt.	qrs.	lbs.	lbs.	=kilos.	gms.	cwt.	qrs.	lbs.	lbs.	=kilos.	gms.
6	0	1	673	305	254	6	1	1	701	317	954
6	0	2	674	305	707	6	1	2	702	318	407
6	0	3	675	306	161	6	1	3	703	318	861
6	0	4	676	306	614	6	1	4	704	319	314
6	0	5	677	307	068	6	1	5	705	319	768
6	0	6	678	307	521	6	1	6	706	320	221
6	0	7	679	307	975	6	1	7	707	320	675
6	0	8	680	308	429	6	1	8	708	321	129
6	0	9	681	308	882	6	1	9	709	321	582
6	0	10	682	309	336	6	1	10	710	322	036
6	0	11	683	309	789	6	1	11	711	322	489
6	0	12	684	310	243	6	1	12	712	322	943
6	0	13	685	310	696	6	1	13	713	323	396
6	0	14	49 686	311	150	6	1	14	51 714	323	850
6	0	15	687	311	604	6	1	15	715	324	304
6	0	16	688	312	057	6	1	16	716	324	757
6	0	17	689	312	511	6	1	17	717	325	211
6	0	18	690	312	964	6	1	18	718	325	664
6	0	19	691	313	418	6	1	19	719	326	118
6	0	20	692	313	871	6	1	20	720	326	571
6	0	21	693	314	325	6	1	21	721	327	025
6	0	22	694	314	779	6	1	22	722	327	479
6	0	23	695	315	232	6	1	23	723	327	932
6	0	24	696	315	686	6	1	24	724	328	386
6	0	25	697	316	139	6	1	25	725	328	839
6	0	26	698	316	593	6	1	26	726	329	293
6	0	27	699	317	046	6	1	27	727	329	746
6	1	0	50 700	317	500	6	2	0	52 728	330	200

T.	c.	q.	lb.	lbs.	=kilos.	gms.	T.	c.	q.	lb.	lbs.	=kilos.	gms.
0	4	1	24	500	226	796	4	9	1	4	10,000	4,535	924
0	8	3	20	1000	453	592	4	18	0	24	11,000	4,989	517
0	13	1	16	1500	680	389	5	7	0	16	12,000	5,443	109
0	17	3	12	2000	907	185	5	16	0	8	13,000	5,896	701
1	6	3	4	3000	1,360	777	6	5	0	0	14,000	6,350	294
1	15	2	24	4000	1,814	370	6	13	3	20	15,000	6,803	886
2	4	2	16	5000	2,267	962	7	2	3	12	16,000	7,257	479
2	13	2	8	6000	2,721	554	7	11	3	4	17,000	7,711	071
3	2	2	0	7000	3,175	147	8	0	2	24	18,000	8,164	663
3	11	1	20	8000	3,628	739	8	9	2	16	19,000	8,618	256
4	0	1	12	9000	4,082	332	8	18	2	8	20,000	9,071	848

cwt.	qrs.	lbs.	lbs.	=kilos.	gms.	cwt.	qrs.	lbs.	lbs.	=kilos.	gms.
6	2	1	729	330	654	6	3	1	757	343	354
6	2	2	730	331	107	6	3	2	758	343	807
6	2	3	731	331	561	6	3	3	759	344	261
6	2	4	732	332	014	6	3	4	760	344	714
6	2	5	733	332	468	6	3	5	761	345	168
6	2	6	734	332	921	6	3	6	762	345	621
6	2	7	735	333	375	6	3	7	763	346	075
6	2	8	736	333	829	6	3	8	764	346	529
6	2	9	737	334	282	6	3	9	765	346	982
6	2	10	738	334	736	6	3	10	766	347	436
6	2	11	739	335	189	6	3	11	767	347	889
6	2	12	*Stones.* 740	335	643	6	3	12	*Stones.* 768	348	343
6	2	13	741	336	096	6	3	13	769	348	796
6	2	14	53 742	336	550	6	3	14	55 770	349	250
6	2	15	743	337	004	6	3	15	771	349	704
6	2	16	744	337	457	6	3	16	772	350	157
6	2	17	745	337	911	6	3	17	773	350	611
6	2	18	746	338	364	6	3	18	774	351	064
6	2	19	747	338	818	6	3	19	775	351	518
6	2	20	748	339	271	6	3	20	776	351	971
6	2	21	749	339	725	6	3	21	777	352	425
6	2	22	750	340	179	6	3	22	778	352	879
6	2	23	751	340	632	6	3	23	779	353	332
6	2	24	752	341	086	6	3	24	780	353	786
6	2	25	753	341	539	6	3	25	781	354	239
6	2	26	*Stones.* 754	341	993	6	3	26	*Stones.* 782	354	693
6	2	27	755	342	446	6	3	27	783	355	146
6	3	0	54 756	342	900	7	0	0	56 784	355	600

=lbs.	Tons	=kilos.	gms.	=lbs.	Tons	=kilos.	gms.
560	¼	254	012	12,320	5½	5,588	258
1,120	½	508	023	13,440	6	6,096	282
2,240	1	1,016	047	14,560	6½	6,604	305
3,360	1½	1,524	070	15,680	7	7,112	329
4,480	2	2,032	094	16,800	7½	7,620	352
5,600	2½	2,540	117	17,920	8	8,128	376
6,720	3	3,048	141	19,040	8½	8,636	399
7,840	3½	3,556	164	20,160	9	9,144	423
8,960	4	4,064	188	21,280	9½	9,652	446
10,080	4½	4,572	211	22,400	10	10,160	470
11,200	5	5,080	235	24,640	11	11,176	517

cwt.	qrs.	lbs.	lbs.	=kilos.	gms.	cwt.	qrs.	lbs.	lbs.	=kilos.	gms.
7	0	1	785	356	054	7	1	1	813	368	754
7	0	2	786	356	507	7	1	2	814	369	207
7	0	3	787	356	961	7	1	3	815	369	661
7	0	4	788	357	414	7	1	4	816	370	114
7	0	5	789	357	868	7	1	5	817	370	568
7	0	6	790	358	321	7	1	6	818	371	021
7	0	7	791	358	775	7	1	7	819	371	475
7	0	8	792	359	229	7	1	8	820	371	929
7	0	9	793	359	682	7	1	9	821	372	382
7	0	10	794	360	136	7	1	10	822	372	836
7	0	11	795	360	589	7	1	11	823	373	289
7	0	12	Stones. 796	361	043	7	1	12	Stones. 824	373	743
7	0	13	797	361	496	7	1	13	825	374	196
7	0	14	57 798	361	950	7	1	14	59 826	374	650
7	0	15	799	362	404	7	1	15	827	375	104
7	0	16	800	362	857	7	1	16	828	375	557
7	0	17	801	363	311	7	1	17	829	376	011
7	0	18	802	363	764	7	1	18	830	376	464
7	0	19	803	364	218	7	1	19	831	376	918
7	0	20	804	364	671	7	1	20	832	377	371
7	0	21	805	365	125	7	1	21	833	377	825
7	0	22	806	365	579	7	1	22	834	378	279
7	0	23	807	366	032	7	1	23	835	378	732
7	0	24	808	366	486	7	1	24	836	379	186
7	0	25	809	366	939	7	1	25	837	379	639
7	0	26	Stones. 810	367	393	7	1	26	Stones. 838	380	093
7	0	27	Stones. 811	367	846	7	1	27	Stones. 839	380	546
7	1	0	58 812	368	300	7	2	0	60 840	381	000

T.	c.	q.	lb.	lbs.	=kilos.	gms.	T.	c.	q.	lb.	lbs.	=kilos.	gms.
0	4	1	24	500	226	796	4	9	1	4	10,000	4,535	924
0	8	3	20	1000	453	592	4	18	0	24	11,000	4,989	517
0	13	1	16	1500	680	389	5	7	0	16	12,000	5,443	109
0	17	3	12	2000	907	185	5	16	0	8	13,000	5,896	701
1	6	3	4	3000	1,360	777	6	5	0	0	14,000	6,350	294
1	15	2	24	4000	1,814	370	6	13	3	20	15,000	6,803	886
2	4	2	16	5000	2,267	962	7	2	3	12	16,000	7,257	479
2	13	2	8	6000	2,721	554	7	11	3	4	17,000	7,711	071
3	2	2	0	7000	3,175	147	8	0	2	24	18,000	8,164	663
3	11	1	20	8000	3,628	739	8	9	2	16	19,000	8,618	256
4	0	1	12	9000	4,082	332	8	18	2	8	20,000	9,071	848

cwt.	qrs.	lbs.	lbs.	=kilos.	gms.	cwt.	qrs.	lbs.	lbs.	=kilos.	gms.
7	2	1	841	381	454	7	3	1	869	394	154
7	2	2	842	381	907	7	3	2	870	394	607
7	2	3	843	382	361	7	3	3	871	395	061
7	2	4	844	382	814	7	3	4	872	395	514
7	2	5	845	383	268	7	3	5	873	395	968
7	2	6	846	383	721	7	3	6	874	396	421
7	2	7	847	384	175	7	3	7	875	396	875
7	2	8	848	384	629	7	3	8	876	397	329
7	2	9	849	385	082	7	3	9	877	397	782
7	2	10	850	385	536	7	3	10	878	398	236
7	2	11	851	385	989	7	3	11	879	398	689
7	2	12	852	386	443	7	3	12	880	399	143
7	2	13	853	386	896	7	3	13	881	399	596
7	2	14	61 854	387	350	7	3	14	63 882	400	050
7	2	15	855	387	804	7	3	15	883	400	504
7	2	16	856	388	257	7	3	16	884	400	957
7	2	17	857	388	711	7	3	17	885	401	411
7	2	18	858	389	164	7	3	18	886	401	864
7	2	19	859	389	618	7	3	19	887	402	318
7	2	20	860	390	071	7	3	20	888	402	771
7	2	21	861	390	525	7	3	21	889	403	225
7	2	22	862	390	979	7	3	22	890	403	679
7	2	23	863	391	432	7	3	23	891	404	132
7	2	24	864	391	886	7	3	24	892	404	586
7	2	25	865	392	339	7	3	25	893	405	039
7	2	26	866	392	793	7	3	26	894	405	493
7	2	27	867	393	246	7	3	27	895	405	946
7	3	0	62 868	393	700	8	0	0	64 896	406	400

=lbs.	Tons	=kilos.	gms.	=lbs.	Tons	=kilos.	gms.
560	¼	254	012	12,320	5½	5,588	258
1,120	½	508	023	13,440	6	6,096	282
2,240	1	1,016	047	14,560	6½	6,604	305
3,360	1½	1,524	070	15,680	7	7,112	329
4,480	2	2,032	094	16,800	7½	7,620	352
5,600	2½	2,540	117	17,920	8	8,128	376
6,720	3	3,048	141	19,040	8½	8,636	399
7,840	3½	3,556	164	20,160	9	9,144	423
8,960	4	4,064	188	21,280	9½	9,652	446
10,080	4½	4,572	211	22,400	10	10,160	470
11,200	5	5,080	235	24,640	11	11,176	517

LBS. = TONS, CWTS., QRS., & KILOS. (1016 kg.)

cwt.	qrs.	lbs.	lbs.	=kilos.	gms.	cwt.	qrs.	lbs.	lbs.	=kilos.	gms.
8	0	1	897	406	854	8	1	1	925	419	554
8	0	2	898	407	307	8	1	2	926	420	007
8	0	3	899	407	761	8	1	3	927	420	461
8	0	4	900	408	214	8	1	4	928	420	914
8	0	5	901	408	668	8	1	5	929	421	368
8	0	6	902	409	121	8	1	6	930	421	821
8	0	7	903	409	575	8	1	7	931	422	275
8	0	8	904	410	029	8	1	8	932	422	729
8	0	9	905	410	482	8	1	9	933	423	182
8	0	10	906	410	936	8	1	10	934	423	636
8	0	11	907	411	389	8	1	11	935	424	089
8	0	12	908	411	843	8	1	12	936	424	543
8	0	13	909	412	296	8	1	13	937	424	996
8	0	14	65 910	412	750	8	1	14	67 938	425	450
8	0	15	911	413	204	8	1	15	939	425	904
8	0	16	912	413	657	8	1	16	940	426	357
8	0	17	913	414	111	8	1	17	941	426	811
8	0	18	914	414	564	8	1	18	942	427	264
8	0	19	915	415	018	8	1	19	943	427	718
8	0	20	916	415	471	8	1	20	944	428	171
8	0	21	917	415	925	8	1	21	945	428	625
8	0	22	918	416	379	8	1	22	946	429	079
8	0	23	919	416	832	8	1	23	947	429	532
8	0	24	920	417	286	8	1	24	948	429	986
8	0	25	921	417	739	8	1	25	949	430	439
8	0	26	922	418	193	8	1	26	950	430	893
8	0	27	923	418	646	8	1	27	951	431	346
8	1	0	66 924	419	100	8	2	0	68 952	431	800

T.	c.	q.	lb.	lbs.	=kilos.	gms.	T.	c.	q.	lb.	lbs.	=kilos.	gms.
0	4	1	24	500	226	796	4	9	1	4	10,000	4,535	924
0	8	3	20	1000	453	592	4	18	0	24	11,000	4,989	517
0	13	1	16	1500	680	389	5	7	0	16	12,000	5,443	109
0	17	3	12	2000	907	185	5	16	0	8	13,000	5,896	701
1	6	3	4	3000	1,360	777	6	5	0	0	14,000	6,350	294
1	15	2	24	4000	1,814	370	6	13	3	20	15,000	6,803	886
2	4	2	16	5000	2,267	962	7	2	3	12	16,000	7,257	479
2	13	2	8	6000	2,721	554	7	11	3	4	17,000	7,711	071
3	2	2	0	7000	3,175	147	8	0	2	24	18,000	8,164	663
3	11	1	20	8000	3,628	739	8	9	2	16	19,000	8,618	256
4	0	1	12	9000	4,082	332	8	18	2	8	20,000	9,071	848

cwt.	qrs.	lbs.	lbs.	=kilos.	gms.	cwt.	qrs.	lbs.	lbs.	=kilos.	gms.
8	2	1	953	432	254	8	3	1	981	444	954
8	2	2	954	432	707	8	3	2	982	445	407
8	2	3	955	433	161	8	3	3	983	445	861
8	2	4	956	433	614	8	3	4	984	446	314
8	2	5	957	434	068	8	3	5	985	446	768
8	2	6	958	434	521	8	3	6	986	447	221
8	2	7	959	434	975	8	3	7	987	447	675
8	2	8	960	435	429	8	3	8	988	448	129
8	2	9	961	435	882	8	3	9	989	448	582
8	2	10	962	436	336	8	3	10	990	449	036
8	2	11	963	436	789	8	3	11	991	449	489
8	2	12	*Stones.* 964	437	243	8	3	12	*Stones.* 992	449	943
8	2	13	965	437	696	8	3	13	993	450	396
8	2	14	69 966	438	150	8	3	14	71 994	450	850
8	2	15	967	438	604	8	3	15	995	451	304
8	2	16	968	439	057	8	3	16	996	451	757
8	2	17	969	439	511	8	3	17	997	452	211
8	2	18	970	439	964	8	3	18	998	452	664
8	2	19	971	440	418	8	3	19	999	453	118
8	2	20	972	440	871	8	3	20	1000	453	571
8	2	21	973	441	325	8	3	21	1001	454	025
8	2	22	974	441	779	8	3	22	1002	454	479
8	2	23	975	442	232	8	3	23	1003	454	932
8	2	24	976	442	686	8	3	24	1004	455	386
8	2	25	977	443	139	8	3	25	1005	455	839
8	2	26	*Stones.* 978	443	593	8	3	26	1006	456	293
8	2	27	*Stones.* 979	444	046	8	3	27	1007	456	746
8	3	0	70 980	444	500	9	0	0	1008	457	200

=lbs.	Tons	=kilos.	gms.	=lbs.	Tons	=kilos.	gms.
560	¼	254	012	12,320	5½	5,588	258
1,120	½	508	023	13,440	6	6,096	282
2,240	1	1,016	047	14,560	6½	6,604	305
3,360	1½	1,524	070	15,680	7	7,112	329
4,480	2	2,032	094	16,800	7½	7,620	352
5,600	2½	2,540	117	17,920	8	8,128	376
6,720	3	3,048	141	19,040	8½	8,636	399
7,840	3½	3,556	164	20,160	9	9,144	423
8,960	4	4,064	188	21,280	9½	9,652	446
10,080	4½	4,572	211	22,400	10	10,160	470
11,200	5	5,080	235	24,640	11	11,176	517

70.   LBS. = TONS, CWTS., QRS., & KILOS.

cwt.	qrs.	lbs.	lbs.	=kilos.	gms.	cwt.	qrs.	lbs.	lbs.	=kilos.	gms.
9	0	1	1009	457	654	9	1	1	1037	470	354
9	0	2	1010	458	107	9	1	2	1038	470	807
9	0	3	1011	458	561	9	1	3	1039	471	261
9	0	4	1012	459	014	9	1	4	1040	471	714
9	0	5	1013	459	468	9	1	5	1041	472	168
9	0	6	1014	459	921	9	1	6	1042	472	621
9	0	7	1015	460	375	9	1	7	1043	473	075
9	0	8	1016	460	829	9	1	8	1044	473	529
9	0	9	1017	461	282	9	1	9	1045	473	982
9	0	10	1018	461	736	9	1	10	1046	474	436
9	0	11	1019	462	189	9	1	11	1047	474	889
9	0	12	1020	462	643	9	1	12	1048	475	343
9	0	13	1021	463	096	9	1	13	1049	475	796
9	0	14	1022	463	550	9	1	14	1050	476	250
9	0	15	1023	464	004	9	1	15	1051	476	704
9	0	16	1024	464	457	9	1	16	1052	477	157
9	0	17	1025	464	911	9	1	17	1053	477	611
9	0	18	1026	465	364	9	1	18	1054	478	064
9	0	19	1027	465	818	9	1	19	1055	478	518
9	0	20	1028	466	271	9	1	20	1056	478	971
9	0	21	1029	466	725	9	1	21	1057	479	425
9	0	22	1030	467	179	9	1	22	1058	479	879
9	0	23	1031	467	632	9	1	23	1059	480	332
9	0	24	1032	468	086	9	1	24	1060	480	786
9	0	25	1033	468	539	9	1	25	1061	481	239
9	0	26	1034	468	993	9	1	26	1062	481	693
9	0	27	1035	469	446	9	1	27	1063	482	146
9	1	0	1036	469	900	9	2	0	1064	482	600

T.	c.	q.	lb.	lbs.	=kilos.	gms.	T.	c.	q.	lb.	lbs.	=kilos.	gms.
0	4	1	24	500	226	796	4	9	1	4	10,000	4,535	924
0	8	3	20	1000	453	592	4	18	0	24	11,000	4,989	517
0	13	1	16	1500	680	389	5	7	0	16	12,000	5,443	109
0	17	3	12	2000	907	185	5	16	0	8	13,000	5,896	701
1	6	3	4	3000	1,360	777	6	5	0	0	14,000	6,350	294
1	15	2	24	4000	1,814	370	6	13	3	20	15,000	6,803	886
2	4	2	16	5000	2,267	962	7	2	3	12	16,000	7,257	479
2	13	2	8	6000	2,721	554	7	11	3	4	17,000	7,711	071
3	2	2	0	7000	3,175	147	8	0	2	24	18,000	8,164	663
3	11	1	20	8000	3,628	739	8	9	2	16	19,000	8,618	256
4	0	1	12	9000	4,082	332	8	18	2	8	20,000	9,071	848

cwt.	qrs.	lbs.	lbs.	=kilos.	gms.	cwt.	qrs.	lbs.	lbs.	=kilos.	gms.
9	2	1	1065	483	054	9	3	1	1093	495	754
9	2	2	1066	483	507	9	3	2	1094	496	207
9	2	3	1067	483	961	9	3	3	1095	496	661
9	2	4	1068	484	414	9	3	4	1096	497	114
9	2	5	1069	484	868	9	3	5	1097	497	568
9	2	6	1070	485	321	9	3	6	1098	498	021
9	2	7	1071	485	775	9	3	7	1099	498	475
9	2	8	1072	486	229	9	3	8	1100	498	929
9	2	9	1073	486	682	9	3	9	1101	499	382
9	2	10	1074	487	136	9	3	10	1102	499	836
9	2	11	1075	487	589	9	3	11	1103	500	289
9	2	12	1076	488	043	9	3	12	1104	500	743
9	2	13	1077	488	496	9	3	13	1105	501	196
9	2	14	1078	488	950	9	3	14	1106	501	650
9	2	15	1079	489	404	9	3	15	1107	502	104
9	2	16	1080	489	857	9	3	16	1108	502	557
9	2	17	1081	490	311	9	3	17	1109	503	011
9	2	18	1082	490	764	9	3	18	1110	503	464
9	2	19	1083	491	218	9	3	19	1111	503	918
9	2	20	1084	491	671	9	3	20	1112	504	371
9	2	21	1085	492	125	9	3	21	1113	504	825
9	2	22	1086	492	579	9	3	22	1114	505	279
9	2	23	1087	493	032	9	3	23	1115	505	732
9	2	24	1088	493	486	9	3	24	1116	506	186
9	2	25	1089	493	939	9	3	25	1117	506	639
9	2	26	1090	494	393	9	3	26	1118	507	093
9	2	27	1091	494	846	9	3	27	1119	507	546
9	3	0	1092	495	300	10	0	0	1120	508	000

=lbs.	Tons	=kilos.	gms.	=lbs.	Tons	=kilos.	gms.
560	¼	254	012	12,320	5½	5,588	258
1,120	½	508	023	13,440	6	6,096	282
2,240	1	1,016	047	14,560	6½	6,604	305
3,360	1½	1,524	070	15,680	7	7,112	329
4,480	2	2,032	094	16,800	7½	7,620	352
5,600	2½	2,540	117	17,920	8	8,128	376
6,720	3	3,048	141	19,040	8½	8,636	399
7,840	3½	3,556	164	20,160	9	9,144	423
8,960	4	4,064	188	21,280	9½	9,652	446
10,080	4½	4,572	211	22,400	10	10,160	470
11,200	5	5,080	235	24,640	11	11,176	517

LBS. = TONS, CWTS., QRS., & KILOS.

cwt.	qrs.	lbs.	lbs.	=kilos.	gms.	cwt.	qrs.	lbs.	lbs.	=kilos.	gms.
10	0	1	1121	508	454	10	1	1	1149	521	154
10	0	2	1122	508	907	10	1	2	1150	521	607
10	0	3	1123	509	361	10	1	3	1151	522	061
10	0	4	1124	509	814	10	1	4	1152	522	514
10	0	5	1125	510	268	10	1	5	1153	522	968
10	0	6	1126	510	721	10	1	6	1154	523	421
10	0	7	1127	511	175	10	1	7	1155	523	875
10	0	8	1128	511	629	10	1	8	1156	524	329
10	0	9	1129	512	082	10	1	9	1157	524	782
10	0	10	1130	512	536	10	1	10	1158	525	236
10	0	11	1131	512	989	10	1	11	1159	525	689
10	0	12	1132	513	443	10	1	12	1160	526	143
10	0	13	1133	513	896	10	1	13	1161	526	596
10	0	14	1134	514	350	10	1	14	1162	527	050
10	0	15	1135	514	804	10	1	15	1163	527	504
10	0	16	1136	515	257	10	1	16	1164	527	957
10	0	17	1137	515	711	10	1	17	1165	528	411
10	0	18	1138	516	164	10	1	18	1166	528	864
10	0	19	1139	516	618	10	1	19	1167	529	318
10	0	20	1140	517	071	10	1	20	1168	529	771
10	0	21	1141	517	525	10	1	21	1169	530	225
10	0	22	1142	517	979	10	1	22	1170	530	679
10	0	23	1143	518	432	10	1	23	1171	531	132
10	0	24	1144	518	886	10	1	24	1172	531	586
10	0	25	1145	519	339	10	1	25	1173	532	039
10	0	26	1146	519	793	10	1	26	1174	532	493
10	0	27	1147	520	246	10	1	27	1175	532	946
10	1	0	1148	520	700	10	2	0	1176	533	400

T.	c.	q.	lb.	lbs.	=kilos.	gms.	T.	c.	q.	lb.	lbs.	=kilos.	gms.
0	4	1	24	500	226	796	4	9	1	4	10,000	4,535	924
0	8	3	20	1000	453	592	4	18	0	24	11,000	4,989	517
0	13	1	16	1500	680	389	5	7	0	16	12,000	5,443	109
0	17	3	12	2000	907	185	5	16	0	8	13,000	5,896	701
1	6	3	4	3000	1,360	777	6	5	0	0	14,000	6,350	294
1	15	2	24	4000	1,814	370	6	13	3	20	15,000	6,803	886
2	4	2	16	5000	2,267	962	7	2	3	12	16,000	7,257	479
2	13	2	8	6000	2,721	554	7	11	3	4	17,000	7,711	071
3	2	2	0	7000	3,175	147	8	0	2	24	18,000	8,164	663
3	11	1	20	8000	3,628	739	8	9	2	16	19,000	8,618	256
4	0	1	12	9000	4,082	332	8	18	2	8	20,000	9,071	848

cwt.	qrs.	lbs.	lbs.	=kilos.	gms.	cwt.	qrs.	lbs.	lbs.	=kilos.	gms.
10	2	1	1177	533	854	10	3	1	1205	546	554
10	2	2	1178	534	307	10	3	2	1206	547	007
10	2	3	1179	534	761	10	3	3	1207	547	461
10	2	4	1180	535	214	10	3	4	1208	547	914
10	2	5	1181	535	668	10	3	5	1209	548	368
10	2	6	1182	536	121	10	3	6	1210	548	821
10	2	7	1183	536	575	10	3	7	1211	549	275
10	2	8	1184	537	029	10	3	8	1212	549	729
10	2	9	1185	537	482	10	3	9	1213	550	182
10	2	10	1186	537	936	10	3	10	1214	550	636
10	2	11	1187	538	389	10	3	11	1215	551	089
10	2	12	1188	538	843	10	3	12	1216	551	543
10	2	13	1189	539	296	10	3	13	1217	551	996
10	2	14	1190	539	750	10	3	14	1218	552	450
10	2	15	1191	540	204	10	3	15	1219	552	904
10	2	16	1192	540	657	10	3	16	1220	553	357
10	2	17	1193	541	111	10	3	17	1221	553	811
10	2	18	1194	541	564	10	3	18	1222	554	264
10	2	19	1195	542	018	10	3	19	1223	554	718
10	2	20	1196	542	471	10	3	20	1224	555	171
10	2	21	1197	542	925	10	3	21	1225	555	625
10	2	22	1198	543	379	10	3	22	1226	556	079
10	2	23	1199	543	832	10	3	23	1227	556	532
10	2	24	1200	544	286	10	3	24	1228	556	986
10	2	25	1201	544	739	10	3	25	1229	557	439
10	2	26	1202	545	193	10	3	26	1230	557	893
10	2	27	1203	545	646	10	3	27	1231	558	346
10	3	0	1204	546	100	11	0	0	1232	558	800

=lbs.	Tons	=kilos.	gms.	=lbs.	Tons	=kilos.	gms.
560	¼	254	012	12,320	5½	5,588	258
1,120	½	508	023	13,440	6	6,096	282
2,240	1	1,016	047	14,560	6½	6,604	305
3,360	1½	1,524	070	15,680	7	7,112	329
4,480	2	2,032	094	16,800	7½	7,620	352
5,600	2½	2,540	117	17,920	8	8,128	376
6,720	3	3,048	141	19,040	8½	8,636	399
7,840	3½	3,556	164	20,160	9	9,144	423
8,960	4	4,064	188	21,280	9½	9,652	446
10,080	4½	4,572	211	22,400	10	10,160	470
11,200	5	5,080	235	24,640	11	11,176	517

F

LBS. = TONS, CWTS., QRS., & KILOS.

cwt.	qrs.	lbs.	lbs.	=kilos.	gms.	cwt.	qrs.	lbs.	lbs.	=kilos.	gms.
11	0	1	1233	559	254	11	1	1	1261	571	954
11	0	2	1234	559	707	11	1	2	1262	572	407
11	0	3	1235	560	161	11	1	3	1263	572	861
11	0	4	1236	560	614	11	1	4	1264	573	314
11	0	5	1237	561	068	11	1	5	1265	573	768
11	0	6	1238	561	521	11	1	6	1266	574	221
11	0	7	1239	561	975	11	1	7	1267	574	675
11	0	8	1240	562	429	11	1	8	1268	575	129
11	0	9	1241	562	882	11	1	9	1269	575	582
11	0	10	1242	563	336	11	1	10	1270	576	036
11	0	11	1243	563	789	11	1	11	1271	576	489
11	0	12	1244	564	243	11	1	12	1272	576	943
11	0	13	1245	564	696	11	1	13	1273	577	396
11	0	14	1246	565	150	11	1	14	1274	577	850
11	0	15	1247	565	604	11	1	15	1275	578	304
11	0	16	1248	566	057	11	1	16	1276	578	757
11	0	17	1249	566	511	11	1	17	1277	579	211
11	0	18	1250	566	964	11	1	18	1278	579	664
11	0	19	1251	567	418	11	1	19	1279	580	118
11	0	20	1252	567	871	11	1	20	1280	580	571
11	0	21	1253	568	325	11	1	21	1281	581	025
11	0	22	1254	568	779	11	1	22	1282	581	479
11	0	23	1255	569	232	11	1	23	1283	581	932
11	0	24	1256	569	686	11	1	24	1284	582	386
11	0	25	1257	570	139	11	1	25	1285	582	839
11	0	26	1258	570	593	11	1	26	1286	583	293
11	0	27	1259	571	046	11	1	27	1287	583	746
11	1	0	1260	571	500	11	2	0	1288	584	200

T.	c.	q.	lb.	lbs.	=kilos.	gms.	T.	c.	q.	lb.	lbs.	=kilos.	gms.
0	4	1	24	500	226	796	4	9	1	4	10,000	4,535	924
0	8	3	20	1000	453	592	4	18	0	24	11,000	4,989	517
0	13	1	16	1500	680	389	5	7	0	16	12,000	5,443	109
0	17	3	12	2000	907	185	5	16	0	8	13,000	5,896	701
1	6	3	4	3000	1,360	777	6	5	0	0	14,000	6,350	294
1	15	2	24	4000	1,814	370	6	13	3	20	15,000	6,803	886
2	4	2	16	5000	2,267	962	7	2	3	12	16,000	7,257	479
2	13	2	8	6000	2,721	554	7	11	3	4	17,000	7,711	071
3	2	2	0	7000	3,175	147	8	0	2	24	18,000	8,164	663
3	11	1	20	8000	3,628	739	8	9	2	16	19,000	8,618	256
4	0	1	12	9000	4,082	332	8	18	2	8	20,000	9,071	848

cwt.	qrs.	lbs.	lbs.	=kilos.	gms.	cwt.	qrs.	lbs.	lbs.	=kilos.	gms.
11	2	1	1289	584	654	11	3	1	1317	597	354
11	2	2	1290	585	107	11	3	2	1318	597	807
11	2	3	1291	585	561	11	3	3	1319	598	261
11	2	4	1292	586	014	11	3	4	1320	598	714
11	2	5	1293	586	468	11	3	5	1321	599	168
11	2	6	1294	586	921	11	3	6	1322	599	621
11	2	7	1295	587	375	11	3	7	1323	600	075
11	2	8	1296	587	829	11	3	8	1324	600	529
11	2	9	1297	588	282	11	3	9	1325	600	982
11	2	10	1298	588	736	11	3	10	1326	601	436
11	2	11	1299	589	189	11	3	11	1327	601	889
11	2	12	1300	589	643	11	3	12	1328	602	343
11	2	13	1301	590	096	11	3	13	1329	602	796
11	2	14	1302	590	550	11	3	14	1330	603	250
11	2	15	1303	591	004	11	3	15	1331	603	704
11	2	16	1304	591	457	11	3	16	1332	604	157
11	2	17	1305	591	911	11	3	17	1333	604	611
11	2	18	1306	592	364	11	3	18	1334	605	064
11	2	19	1307	592	818	11	3	19	1335	605	518
11	2	20	1308	593	271	11	3	20	1336	605	971
11	2	21	1309	593	725	11	3	21	1337	606	425
11	2	22	1310	594	179	11	3	22	1338	606	879
11	2	23	1311	594	632	11	3	23	1339	607	332
11	2	24	1312	595	086	11	3	24	1340	607	786
11	2	25	1313	595	539	11	3	25	1341	608	239
11	2	26	1314	595	993	11	3	26	1342	608	693
11	2	27	1315	596	446	11	3	27	1343	609	146
11	3	0	1316	596	900	12	0	0	1344	609	600

=lbs.	Tons	=kilos.	gms.	=lbs.	Tons	=kilos.	gms.
560	¼	254	012	12,320	5½	5,588	258
1,120	½	508	023	13,440	6	6,096	282
2,240	1	1,016	047	14,560	6½	6,604	305
3,360	1½	1,524	070	15,680	7	7,112	329
4,480	2	2,032	094	16,800	7½	7,620	352
5,600	2½	2,540	117	17,920	8	8,128	376
6,720	3	3,048	141	19,040	8½	8,636	399
7,840	3½	3,556	164	20,160	9	9,144	423
8,960	4	4,064	188	21,280	9½	9,652	446
10,080	4½	4,572	211	22,400	10	10,160	470
11,200	5	5,080	235	24,640	11	11,176	517

cwt.	qrs.	lbs.	lbs.	=kilos.	gms.	cwt.	qrs.	lbs.	lbs.	=kilos.	gms.
12	0	1	1345	610	054	12	1	1	1373	622	754
12	0	2	1346	610	507	12	1	2	1374	623	207
12	0	3	1347	610	961	12	1	3	1375	623	661
12	0	4	1348	611	414	12	1	4	1376	624	114
12	0	5	1349	611	868	12	1	5	1377	624	568
12	0	6	1350	612	321	12	1	6	1378	625	021
12	0	7	1351	612	775	12	1	7	1379	625	475
12	0	8	1352	613	229	12	1	8	1380	625	929
12	0	9	1353	613	682	12	1	9	1381	626	382
12	0	10	1354	614	136	12	1	10	1382	626	836
12	0	11	1355	614	589	12	1	11	1383	627	289
12	0	12	1356	615	043	12	1	12	1384	627	743
12	0	13	1357	615	496	12	1	13	1385	628	196
12	0	14	1358	615	950	12	1	14	1386	628	650
12	0	15	1359	616	404	12	1	15	1387	629	104
12	0	16	1360	616	857	12	1	16	1388	629	557
12	0	17	1361	617	311	12	1	17	1389	630	011
12	0	18	1362	617	764	12	1	18	1390	630	464
12	0	19	1363	618	218	12	1	19	1391	630	918
12	0	20	1364	618	671	12	1	20	1392	631	371
12	0	21	1365	619	125	12	1	21	1393	631	825
12	0	22	1366	619	579	12	1	22	1394	632	279
12	0	23	1367	620	032	12	1	23	1395	632	732
12	0	24	1368	620	486	12	1	24	1396	633	186
12	0	25	1369	620	939	12	1	25	1397	633	639
12	0	26	1370	621	393	12	1	26	1398	634	093
12	0	27	1371	621	846	12	1	27	1399	634	546
12	1	0	1372	622	300	12	2	0	1400	635	000

T.	c.	q.	lb.	lbs.	=kilos.	gms.	T.	c.	q.	lb.	lbs.	=kilos.	gms.
0	4	1	24	500	226	796	4	9	1	4	10,000	4,535	924
0	8	3	20	1000	453	592	4	18	0	24	11,000	4,989	517
0	13	1	16	1500	680	389	5	7	0	16	12,000	5,443	109
0	17	3	12	2000	907	185	5	16	0	8	13,000	5,896	701
1	6	3	4	3000	1,360	777	6	5	0	0	14,000	6,350	294
1	15	2	24	4000	1,814	370	6	13	3	20	15,000	6,803	886
2	4	2	16	5000	2,267	962	7	2	3	12	16,000	7,257	479
2	13	2	8	6000	2,721	554	7	11	3	4	17,000	7,711	071
3	2	2	0	7000	3,175	147	8	0	2	24	18,000	8,164	663
3	11	1	20	8000	3,628	739	8	9	2	16	19,000	8,618	256
4	0	1	12	9000	4,082	332	8	18	2	8	20,000	9,071	848

cwt.	qrs.	lbs.	lbs.	=kilos.	gms.	cwt.	qrs.	lbs.	lbs.	=kilos.	gms.
12	2	1	1401	635	454	12	3	1	1429	648	154
12	2	2	1402	635	907	12	3	2	1430	648	607
12	2	3	1403	636	361	12	3	3	1431	649	061
12	2	4	1404	636	814	12	3	4	1432	649	514
12	2	5	1405	637	268	12	3	5	1433	649	968
12	2	6	1406	637	721	12	3	6	1434	650	421
12	2	7	1407	638	175	12	3	7	1435	650	875
12	2	8	1408	638	629	12	3	8	1436	651	329
12	2	9	1409	639	082	12	3	9	1437	651	782
12	2	10	1410	639	536	12	3	10	1438	652	236
12	2	11	1411	639	989	12	3	11	1439	652	689
12	2	12	1412	640	443	12	3	12	1440	653	143
12	2	13	1413	640	896	12	3	13	1441	653	596
12	2	14	1414	641	350	12	3	14	1442	654	050
12	2	15	1415	641	804	12	3	15	1443	654	504
12	2	16	1416	642	257	12	3	16	1444	654	957
12	2	17	1417	642	711	12	3	17	1445	655	411
12	2	18	1418	643	164	12	3	18	1446	655	864
12	2	19	1419	643	618	12	3	19	1447	656	318
12	2	20	1420	644	071	12	3	20	1448	656	771
12	2	21	1421	644	525	12	3	21	1449	657	225
12	2	22	1422	644	979	12	3	22	1450	657	679
12	2	23	1423	645	432	12	3	23	1451	658	132
12	2	24	1424	645	886	12	3	24	1452	658	586
12	2	25	1425	646	339	12	3	25	1453	659	039
12	2	26	1426	646	793	12	3	26	1454	659	493
12	2	27	1427	647	246	12	3	27	1455	659	946
12	3	0	1428	647	700	13	0	0	1456	660	400

=lbs.	Tons	=kilos.	gms.	=lbs.	Tons	=kilos.	gms.
560	¼	254	012	12,320	5½	5,588	258
1,120	½	508	023	13,440	6	6,096	282
2,240	1	1,016	047	14,560	6½	6,604	305
3,360	1½	1,524	070	15,680	7	7,112	329
4,480	2	2,032	094	16,800	7½	7,620	352
5,600	2½	2,540	117	17,920	8	8,128	376
6,720	3	3,048	141	19,040	8½	8,636	399
7,840	3½	3,556	164	20,160	9	9,144	423
8,960	4	4,064	188	21,280	9½	9,652	446
10,080	4½	4,572	211	22,400	10	10,160	470
11,200	5	5,080	235	24,640	11	11,176	517

cwt.	qrs.	lbs.	lbs.	=kilos.	gms.	cwt.	qrs.	lbs.	lbs.	=kilos.	gms.
13	0	1	1457	660	854	13	1	1	1485	673	554
13	0	2	1458	661	307	13	1	2	1486	674	007
13	0	3	1459	661	761	13	1	3	1487	674	461
13	0	4	1460	662	214	13	1	4	1488	674	914
13	0	5	1461	662	668	13	1	5	1489	675	368
13	0	6	1462	663	121	13	1	6	1490	675	821
13	0	7	1463	663	575	13	1	7	1491	676	275
13	0	8	1464	664	029	13	1	8	1492	676	729
13	0	9	1465	664	482	13	1	9	1493	677	182
13	0	10	1466	664	936	13	1	10	1494	677	636
13	0	11	1467	665	389	13	1	11	1495	678	089
13	0	12	1468	665	843	13	1	12	1496	678	543
13	0	13	1469	666	296	13	1	13	1497	678	996
13	0	14	1470	666	750	13	1	14	1498	679	450
13	0	15	1471	667	204	13	1	15	1499	679	904
13	0	16	1472	667	657	13	1	16	1500	680	357
13	0	17	1473	668	111	13	1	17	1501	680	811
13	0	18	1474	668	564	13	1	18	1502	681	264
13	0	19	1475	669	018	13	1	19	1503	681	718
13	0	20	1476	669	471	13	1	20	1504	682	171
13	0	21	1477	669	925	13	1	21	1505	682	625
13	0	22	1478	670	379	13	1	22	1506	683	079
13	0	23	1479	670	832	13	1	23	1507	683	532
13	0	24	1480	671	286	13	1	24	1508	683	986
13	0	25	1481	671	739	13	1	25	1509	684	439
13	0	26	1482	672	193	13	1	26	1510	684	893
13	0	27	1483	672	646	13	1	27	1511	685	346
13	1	0	1484	673	100	13	2	0	1512	685	800

T.	c.	q.	lb.	lbs.	=kilos.	gms.	T.	c.	q.	lb.	lbs.	=kilos.	gms.
0	4	1	24	500	226	796	4	9	1	4	10,000	4,535	924
0	8	3	20	1000	453	592	4	18	0	24	11,000	4,989	517
0	13	1	16	1500	680	389	5	7	0	16	12,000	5,443	109
0	17	3	12	2000	907	185	5	16	0	8	13,000	5,896	701
1	6	3	4	3000	1,360	777	6	5	0	0	14,000	6,350	294
1	15	2	24	4000	1,814	370	6	13	3	20	15,000	6,803	886
2	4	2	16	5000	2,267	962	7	2	3	12	16,000	7,257	479
2	13	2	8	6000	2,721	554	7	11	3	4	17,000	7,711	071
3	2	2	0	7000	3,175	147	8	0	2	24	18,000	8,164	663
3	11	1	20	8000	3,628	739	8	9	2	16	19,000	8,618	256
4	0	1	12	9000	4,082	332	8	18	2	8	20,000	9,071	848

cwt.	qrs.	lbs.	lbs.	=kilos.	gms.	cwt.	qrs.	lbs.	lbs.	=kilos.	gms.
13	2	1	1513	686	254	13	3	1	1541	698	954
13	2	2	1514	686	707	13	3	2	1542	699	407
13	2	3	1515	687	161	13	3	3	1543	699	861
13	2	4	1516	687	614	13	3	4	1544	700	314
13	2	5	1517	688	068	13	3	5	1545	700	768
13	2	6	1518	688	521	13	3	6	1546	701	221
13	2	7	1519	688	975	13	3	7	1547	701	675
13	2	8	1520	689	429	13	3	8	1548	702	129
13	2	9	1521	689	882	13	3	9	1549	702	582
13	2	10	1522	690	336	13	3	10	1550	703	036
13	2	11	1523	690	789	13	3	11	1551	703	489
13	2	12	1524	691	243	13	3	12	1552	703	943
13	2	13	1525	691	696	13	3	13	1553	704	396
13	2	14	1526	692	150	13	3	14	1554	704	850
13	2	15	1527	692	604	13	3	15	1555	705	304
13	2	16	1528	693	057	13	3	16	1556	705	757
13	2	17	1529	693	511	13	3	17	1557	706	211
13	2	18	1530	693	964	13	3	18	1558	706	664
13	2	19	1531	694	418	13	3	19	1559	707	118
13	2	20	1532	694	871	13	3	20	1560	707	571
13	2	21	1533	695	325	13	3	21	1561	708	025
13	2	22	1534	695	779	13	3	22	1562	708	479
13	2	23	1535	696	232	13	3	23	1563	708	932
13	2	24	1536	696	686	13	3	24	1564	709	386
13	2	25	1537	697	139	13	3	25	1565	709	839
13	2	26	1538	697	593	13	3	26	1566	710	293
13	2	27	1539	698	046	13	3	27	1567	710	746
13	3	0	1540	698	500	14	0	0	1568	711	200

=lbs.	Tons	=kilos.	gms.	=lbs.	Tons	=kilos.	gms.
560	¼	254	012	12,320	5½	5,588	258
1,120	½	508	023	13,440	6	6,096	282
2,240	1	1,016	047	14,560	6½	6,604	305
3,360	1½	1,524	070	15,680	7	7,112	329
4,480	2	2,032	094	16,800	7½	7,620	352
5,600	2½	2,540	117	17,920	8	8,128	376
6,720	3	3,048	141	19,040	8½	8,636	399
7,840	3½	3,556	164	20,160	9	9,144	423
8,960	4	4,064	188	21,280	9½	9,652	446
10,080	4½	4,572	211	22,400	10	10,160	470
11,200	5	5,080	235	24,640	11	11,176	517

LBS. = TONS, CWTS., QRS., & KILOS.

cwt.	qrs.	lbs.	lbs.	=kilos.	gms.	cwt.	qrs.	lbs.	lbs.	=kilos.	gms.
14	0	1	1569	711	654	14	1	1	1597	724	354
14	0	2	1570	712	107	14	1	2	1598	724	807
14	0	3	1571	712	561	14	1	3	1599	725	261
14	0	4	1572	713	014	14	1	4	1600	725	714
14	0	5	1573	713	468	14	1	5	1601	726	168
14	0	6	1574	713	921	14	1	6	1602	726	621
14	0	7	1575	714	375	14	1	7	1603	727	075
14	0	8	1576	714	829	14	1	8	1604	727	529
14	0	9	1577	715	282	14	1	9	1605	727	982
14	0	10	1578	715	736	14	1	10	1606	728	436
14	0	11	1579	716	189	14	1	11	1607	728	889
14	0	12	1580	716	643	14	1	12	1608	729	343
14	0	13	1581	717	096	14	1	13	1609	729	796
14	0	14	1582	717	550	14	1	14	1610	730	250
14	0	15	1583	718	004	14	1	15	1611	730	704
14	0	16	1584	718	457	14	1	16	1612	731	157
14	0	17	1585	718	911	14	1	17	1613	731	611
14	0	18	1586	719	364	14	1	18	1614	732	064
14	0	19	1587	719	818	14	1	19	1615	732	518
14	0	20	1588	720	271	14	1	20	1616	732	971
14	0	21	1589	720	725	14	1	21	1617	733	425
14	0	22	1590	721	179	14	1	22	1618	733	879
14	0	23	1591	721	632	14	1	23	1619	734	332
14	0	24	1592	722	086	14	1	24	1620	734	786
14	0	25	1593	722	539	14	1	25	1621	735	239
14	0	26	1594	722	993	14	1	26	1622	735	693
14	0	27	1595	723	446	14	1	27	1623	736	146
14	1	0	1596	723	900	14	2	0	1624	736	600

T.	c.	q.	lb.	lbs.	=kilos.	gms.	T.	c.	q.	lb.	lbs.	=kilos.	gms.
0	4	1	24	500	226	796	4	9	1	4	10,000	4,535	924
0	8	3	20	1000	453	592	4	18	0	24	11,000	4,989	517
0	13	1	16	1500	680	389	5	7	0	16	12,000	5,443	109
0	17	3	12	2000	907	185	5	16	0	8	13,000	5,896	701
1	6	3	4	3000	1,360	777	6	5	0	0	14,000	6,350	294
1	15	2	24	4000	1,814	370	6	13	3	20	15,000	6,803	886
2	4	2	16	5000	2,267	962	7	2	3	12	16,000	7,257	479
2	13	2	8	6000	2,721	554	7	11	3	4	17,000	7,711	071
3	2	2	0	7000	3,175	147	8	0	2	24	18,000	8,164	663
3	11	1	20	8000	3,628	739	8	9	2	16	19,000	8,618	256
4	0	1	12	9000	4,082	332	8	18	2	8	20,000	9,071	848

cwt.	qrs.	lbs.	lbs.	=kilos.	gms.	cwt.	qrs.	lbs.	lbs.	=kilos.	gms.
14	2	1	1625	737	054	14	3	1	1653	749	754
14	2	2	1626	737	507	14	3	2	1654	750	207
14	2	3	1627	737	961	14	3	3	1655	750	661
14	2	4	1628	738	414	14	3	4	1656	751	114
14	2	5	1629	738	868	14	3	5	1657	751	568
14	2	6	1630	739	321	14	3	6	1658	752	021
14	2	7	1631	739	775	14	3	7	1659	752	475
14	2	8	1632	740	229	14	3	8	1660	752	929
14	2	9	1633	740	682	14	3	9	1661	753	382
14	2	10	1634	741	136	14	3	10	1662	753	836
14	2	11	1635	741	589	14	3	11	1663	754	289
14	2	12	1636	742	043	14	3	12	1664	754	743
14	2	13	1637	742	496	14	3	13	1665	755	196
14	2	14	1638	742	950	14	3	14	1666	755	650
14	2	15	1639	743	404	14	3	15	1667	756	104
14	2	16	1640	743	857	14	3	16	1668	756	557
14	2	17	1641	744	311	14	3	17	1669	757	011
14	2	18	1642	744	764	14	3	18	1670	757	464
14	2	19	1643	745	218	14	3	19	1671	757	918
14	2	20	1644	745	671	14	3	20	1672	758	371
14	2	21	1645	746	125	14	3	21	1673	758	825
14	2	22	1646	746	579	14	3	22	1674	759	279
14	2	23	1647	747	032	14	3	23	1675	759	732
14	2	24	1648	747	486	14	3	24	1676	760	186
14	2	25	1649	747	939	14	3	25	1677	760	639
14	2	26	1650	748	393	14	3	26	1678	761	093
14	2	27	1651	748	846	14	3	27	1679	761	546
14	3	0	1652	749	300	15	0	0	1680	762	000

=lbs.	Tons	=kilos.	gms.	=lbs.	Tons	=kilos.	gms.
560	¼	254	012	12,320	5½	5,588	258
1,120	½	508	023	13,440	6	6,096	282
2,240	1	1,016	047	14,560	6½	6,604	305
3,360	1½	1,524	070	15,680	7	7,112	329
4,480	2	2,032	094	16,800	7½	7,620	352
5,600	2½	2,540	117	17,920	8	8,128	376
6,720	3	3,048	141	19,040	8½	8,636	399
7,840	3½	3,556	164	20,160	9	9,144	423
8,960	4	4,064	188	21,280	9½	9,652	446
10,080	4½	4,572	211	22,400	10	10,160	470
11,200	5	5,080	235	24,640	11	11,176	517

LBS. = TONS, CWTS., QRS., & KILOS.

cwt.	qrs.	lbs.	lbs.	=kilos.	gms.	cwt.	qrs.	lbs.	lbs.	=kilos.	gms.
15	0	1	1681	762	454	15	1	1	1709	775	154
15	0	2	1682	762	907	15	1	2	1710	775	607
15	0	3	1683	763	361	15	1	3	1711	776	061
15	0	4	1684	763	814	15	1	4	1712	776	514
15	0	5	1685	764	268	15	1	5	1713	776	968
15	0	6	1686	764	721	15	1	6	1714	777	421
15	0	7	1687	765	175	15	1	7	1715	777	875
15	0	8	1688	765	629	15	1	8	1716	778	329
15	0	9	1689	766	082	15	1	9	1717	778	782
15	0	10	1690	766	536	15	1	10	1718	779	236
15	0	11	1691	766	989	15	1	11	1719	779	689
15	0	12	1692	767	443	15	1	12	1720	780	143
15	0	13	1693	767	896	15	1	13	1721	780	596
15	0	14	1694	768	350	15	1	14	1722	781	050
15	0	15	1695	768	804	15	1	15	1723	781	504
15	0	16	1696	769	257	15	1	16	1724	781	957
15	0	17	1697	769	711	15	1	17	1725	782	411
15	0	18	1698	770	164	15	1	18	1726	782	864
15	0	19	1699	770	618	15	1	19	1727	783	318
15	0	20	1700	771	071	15	1	20	1728	783	771
15	0	21	1701	771	525	15	1	21	1729	784	225
15	0	22	1702	771	979	15	1	22	1730	784	679
15	0	23	1703	772	432	15	1	23	1731	785	132
15	0	24	1704	772	886	15	1	24	1732	785	586
15	0	25	1705	773	339	15	1	25	1733	786	039
15	0	26	1706	773	793	15	1	26	1734	786	493
15	0	27	1707	774	246	15	1	27	1735	786	946
15	1	0	1708	774	700	15	2	0	1736	787	400

T.	c.	q.	lb.	lbs.	=kilos.	gms.	T.	c.	q.	lb.	lbs.	=kilos.	gms.
0	4	1	24	500	226	796	4	9	1	4	10,000	4,535	924
0	8	3	20	1000	453	592	4	18	0	24	11,000	4,989	517
0	13	1	16	1500	680	389	5	7	0	16	12,000	5,443	109
0	17	3	12	2000	907	185	5	16	0	8	13,000	5,896	701
1	6	3	4	3000	1,360	777	6	5	0	0	14,000	6,350	294
1	15	2	24	4000	1,814	370	6	13	3	20	15,000	6,803	886
2	4	2	16	5000	2,267	962	7	2	3	12	16,000	7,257	479
2	13	2	8	6000	2,721	554	7	11	3	4	17,000	7,711	071
3	2	2	0	7000	3,175	147	8	0	2	24	18,000	8,164	663
3	11	1	20	8000	3,628	739	8	9	2	16	19,000	8,618	256
4	0	1	12	9000	4,082	332	8	18	2	8	20,000	9,071	848

cwt.	qrs.	lbs.	lbs.	=kilos.	gms.	cwt.	qrs.	lbs.	lbs.	=kilos.	gms.
15	2	1	1737	787	854	15	3	1	1765	800	554
15	2	2	1738	788	307	15	3	2	1766	801	007
15	2	3	1739	788	761	15	3	3	1767	801	461
15	2	4	1740	789	214	15	3	4	1768	801	914
15	2	5	1741	789	668	15	3	5	1769	802	368
15	2	6	1742	790	121	15	3	6	1770	802	821
15	2	7	1743	790	575	15	3	7	1771	803	275
15	2	8	1744	791	029	15	3	8	1772	803	729
15	2	9	1745	791	482	15	3	9	1773	804	182
15	2	10	1746	791	936	15	3	10	1774	804	636
15	2	11	1747	792	389	15	3	11	1775	805	089
15	2	12	1748	792	843	15	3	12	1776	805	543
15	2	13	1749	793	296	15	3	13	1777	805	996
15	2	14	1750	793	750	15	3	14	1778	806	450
15	2	15	1751	794	204	15	3	15	1779	806	904
15	2	16	1752	794	657	15	3	16	1780	807	357
15	2	17	1753	795	111	15	3	17	1781	807	811
15	2	18	1754	795	564	15	3	18	1782	808	264
15	2	19	1755	796	018	15	3	19	1783	808	718
15	2	20	1756	796	471	15	3	20	1784	809	171
15	2	21	1757	796	925	15	3	21	1785	809	625
15	2	22	1758	797	379	15	3	22	1786	810	079
15	2	23	1759	797	832	15	3	23	1787	810	532
15	2	24	1760	798	286	15	3	24	1788	810	986
15	2	25	1761	798	739	15	3	25	1789	811	439
15	2	26	1762	799	193	15	3	26	1790	811	893
15	2	27	1763	799	646	15	3	27	1791	812	346
15	3	0	1764	800	100	16	0	0	1792	812	800

=lbs.	Tons	=kilos.	gms.	=lbs.	Tons	=kilos.	gms.
560	¼	254	012	12,320	5½	5,588	258
1,120	½	508	023	13,440	6	6,096	282
2,240	1	1,016	047	14,560	6½	6,604	305
3,360	1½	1,524	070	15,680	7	7,112	329
4,480	2	2,032	094	16,800	7½	7,620	352
5,600	2½	2,540	117	17,920	8	8,128	376
6,720	3	3,048	141	19,040	8½	8,636	399
7,840	3½	3,556	164	20,160	9	9,144	423
8,960	4	4,064	188	21,280	9½	9,652	446
10,080	4½	4,572	211	22,400	10	10,160	470
11,200	5	5,080	235	24,640	11	11,176	517

LBS. = TONS, CWTS., QRS., & KILOS. (1016 kg.)

cwt.	qrs.	lbs.	lbs.	=kilos.	gms.	cwt.	qrs.	lbs.	lbs.	=kilos.	gms.
16	0	1	1793	813	254	16	1	1	1821	825	954
16	0	2	1794	813	707	16	1	2	1822	826	407
16	0	3	1795	814	161	16	1	3	1823	826	861
16	0	4	1796	814	614	16	1	4	1824	827	314
16	0	5	1797	815	068	16	1	5	1825	827	768
16	0	6	1798	815	521	16	1	6	1826	828	221
16	0	7	1799	815	975	16	1	7	1827	828	675
16	0	8	1800	816	429	16	1	8	1828	829	129
16	0	9	1801	816	882	16	1	9	1829	829	582
16	0	10	1802	817	336	16	1	10	1830	830	036
16	0	11	1803	817	789	16	1	11	1831	830	489
16	0	12	1804	818	243	16	1	12	1832	830	943
16	0	13	1805	818	696	16	1	13	1833	831	396
16	0	14	1806	819	150	16	1	14	1834	831	850
16	0	15	1807	819	604	16	1	15	1835	832	304
16	0	16	1808	820	057	16	1	16	1836	832	757
16	0	17	1809	820	511	16	1	17	1837	833	211
16	0	18	1810	820	964	16	1	18	1838	833	664
16	0	19	1811	821	418	16	1	19	1839	834	118
16	0	20	1812	821	871	16	1	20	1840	834	571
16	0	21	1813	822	325	16	1	21	1841	835	025
16	0	22	1814	822	779	16	1	22	1842	835	479
16	0	23	1815	823	232	16	1	23	1843	835	932
16	0	24	1816	823	686	16	1	24	1844	836	386
16	0	25	1817	824	139	16	1	25	1845	836	839
16	0	26	1818	824	593	16	1	26	1846	837	293
16	0	27	1819	825	046	16	1	27	1847	837	746
16	1	0	1820	825	500	16	2	0	1848	838	200

T.	c.	q.	lb.	lbs.	=kilos.	gms.	T.	c.	q.	lb.	lbs.	=kilos.	gms.
0	4	1	24	500	226	796	4	9	1	4	10,000	4,535	924
0	8	3	20	1000	453	592	4	18	0	24	11,000	4,989	517
0	13	1	16	1500	680	389	5	7	0	16	12,000	5,443	109
0	17	3	12	2000	907	185	5	16	0	8	13,000	5,896	701
1	6	3	4	3000	1,360	777	6	5	0	0	14,000	6,350	294
1	15	2	24	4000	1,814	370	6	13	3	20	15,000	6,803	886
2	4	2	16	5000	2,267	962	7	2	3	12	16,000	7,257	479
2	13	2	8	6000	2,721	554	7	11	3	4	17,000	7,711	071
3	2	2	0	7000	3,175	147	8	0	2	24	18,000	8,164	663
3	11	1	20	8000	3,628	739	8	9	2	16	19,000	8,618	256
4	0	1	12	9000	4,082	332	8	18	2	8	20,000	9,071	848

cwt.	qrs.	lbs.	lbs.	=kilos.	gms.	cwt.	qrs.	lbs.	lbs.	=kilos.	gms.
16	2	1	1849	838	654	16	3	1	1877	851	354
16	2	2	1850	839	107	16	3	2	1878	851	807
16	2	3	1851	839	561	16	3	3	1879	852	261
16	2	4	1852	840	014	16	3	4	1880	852	714
16	2	5	1853	840	468	16	3	5	1881	853	168
16	2	6	1854	840	921	16	3	6	1882	853	621
16	2	7	1855	841	375	16	3	7	1883	854	075
16	2	8	1856	841	829	16	3	8	1884	854	529
16	2	9	1857	842	282	16	3	9	1885	854	982
16	2	10	1858	842	736	16	3	10	1886	855	436
16	2	11	1859	843	189	16	3	11	1887	855	889
16	2	12	1860	843	643	16	3	12	1888	856	343
16	2	13	1861	844	096	16	3	13	1889	856	796
16	2	14	1862	844	550	16	3	14	1890	857	250
16	2	15	1863	845	004	16	3	15	1891	857	704
16	2	16	1864	845	457	16	3	16	1892	858	157
16	2	17	1865	845	911	16	3	17	1893	858	611
16	2	18	1866	846	364	16	3	18	1894	859	064
16	2	19	1867	846	818	16	3	19	1895	859	518
16	2	20	1868	847	271	16	3	20	1896	859	971
16	2	21	1869	847	725	16	3	21	1897	860	425
16	2	22	1870	848	179	16	3	22	1898	860	879
16	2	23	1871	848	632	16	3	23	1899	861	332
16	2	24	1872	849	086	16	3	24	1900	861	786
16	2	25	1873	849	539	16	3	25	1901	862	239
16	2	26	1874	849	993	16	3	26	1902	862	693
16	2	27	1875	850	446	16	3	27	1903	863	146
16	3	0	1876	850	900	17	0	0	1904	863	600

=lbs.	Tons	=kilos.	gms.	=lbs.	Tons	=kilos.	gms.
560	¼	254	012	12,320	5½	5,588	258
1,120	½	508	023	13,440	6	6,096	282
2,240	1	1,016	047	14,560	6½	6,604	305
3,360	1½	1,524	070	15,680	7	7,112	329
4,480	2	2,032	094	16,800	7½	7,620	352
5,600	2½	2,540	117	17,920	8	8,128	376
6,720	3	3,048	141	19,040	8½	8,636	399
7,840	3½	3,556	164	20,160	9	9,144	423
8,960	4	4,064	188	21,280	9½	9,652	446
10,080	4½	4,572	211	22,400	10	10,160	470
11,200	5	5,080	235	24,640	11	11,176	517

LBS. = TONS, CWTS., QRS., & KILOS.

cwt.	qrs.	lbs.	lbs.	=kilos.	gms.	cwt.	qrs.	lbs.	lbs.	=kilos.	gms.
17	0	1	1905	864	054	17	1	1	1933	876	754
17	0	2	1906	864	507	17	1	2	1934	877	207
17	0	3	1907	864	961	17	1	3	1935	877	661
17	0	4	1908	865	414	17	1	4	1936	878	114
17	0	5	1909	865	868	17	1	5	1937	878	568
17	0	6	1910	866	321	17	1	6	1938	879	021
17	0	7	1911	866	775	17	1	7	1939	879	475
17	0	8	1912	867	229	17	1	8	1940	879	929
17	0	9	1913	867	682	17	1	9	1941	880	382
17	0	10	1914	868	136	17	1	10	1942	880	836
17	0	11	1915	868	589	17	1	11	1943	881	289
17	0	12	1916	869	043	17	1	12	1944	881	743
17	0	13	1917	869	496	17	1	13	1945	882	196
17	0	14	1918	869	950	17	1	14	1946	882	650
17	0	15	1919	870	404	17	1	15	1947	883	104
17	0	16	1920	870	857	17	1	16	1948	883	557
17	0	17	1921	871	311	17	1	17	1949	884	011
17	0	18	1922	871	764	17	1	18	1950	884	464
17	0	19	1923	872	218	17	1	19	1951	884	918
17	0	20	1924	872	671	17	1	20	1952	885	371
17	0	21	1925	873	125	17	1	21	1953	885	825
17	0	22	1926	873	579	17	1	22	1954	886	279
17	0	23	1927	874	032	17	1	23	1955	886	732
17	0	24	1928	874	486	17	1	24	1956	887	186
17	0	25	1929	874	939	17	1	25	1957	887	639
17	0	26	1930	875	393	17	1	26	1958	888	093
17	0	27	1931	875	846	17	1	27	1959	888	546
17	1	0	1932	876	300	17	2	0	1960	889	000

T.	c.	q.	lb.	lbs.	=kilos.	gms.	T.	c.	q.	lb.	lbs.	=kilos.	gms.
0	4	1	24	500	226	796	4	9	1	4	10,000	4,535	924
0	8	3	20	1000	453	592	4	18	0	24	11,000	4,989	517
0	13	1	16	1500	680	389	5	7	0	16	12,000	5,443	109
0	17	3	12	2000	907	185	5	16	0	8	13,000	5,896	701
1	6	3	4	3000	1,360	777	6	5	0	0	14,000	6,350	294
1	15	2	24	4000	1,814	370	6	13	3	20	15,000	6,803	886
2	4	2	16	5000	2,267	962	7	2	3	12	16,000	7,257	479
2	13	2	8	6000	2,721	554	7	11	3	4	17,000	7,711	071
3	2	2	0	7000	3,175	147	8	0	2	24	18,000	8,164	663
3	11	1	20	8000	3,628	739	8	9	2	16	19,000	8,618	256
4	0	1	12	9000	4,082	332	8	18	2	8	20,000	9,071	848

cwt.	qrs.	lbs.	lbs.	=kilos.	gms.	cwt.	qrs.	lbs.	lbs.	=kilos.	gms.
17	2	1	1961	889	454	17	3	1	1989	902	154
17	2	2	1962	889	907	17	3	2	1990	902	607
17	2	3	1963	890	361	17	3	3	1991	903	061
17	2	4	1964	890	814	17	3	4	1992	903	514
17	2	5	1965	891	268	17	3	5	1993	903	968
17	2	6	1966	891	721	17	3	6	1994	904	421
17	2	7	1967	892	175	17	3	7	1995	904	875
17	2	8	1968	892	629	17	3	8	1996	905	329
17	2	9	1969	893	082	17	3	9	1997	905	782
17	2	10	1970	893	536	17	3	10	1998	906	236
17	2	11	1971	893	989	17	3	11	1999	906	689
17	2	12	1972	894	443	17	3	12	2000	907	143
17	2	13	1973	894	896	17	3	13	2001	907	596
17	2	14	1974	895	350	17	3	14	2002	908	050
17	2	15	1975	895	804	17	3	15	2003	908	504
17	2	16	1976	896	257	17	3	16	2004	908	957
17	2	17	1977	896	711	17	3	17	2005	909	411
17	2	18	1978	897	164	17	3	18	2006	909	864
17	2	19	1979	897	618	17	3	19	2007	910	318
17	2	20	1980	898	071	17	3	20	2008	910	771
17	2	21	1981	898	525	17	3	21	2009	911	225
17	2	22	1982	898	979	17	3	22	2010	911	679
17	2	23	1983	899	432	17	3	23	2011	912	132
17	2	24	1984	899	886	17	3	24	2012	912	586
17	2	25	1985	900	339	17	3	25	2013	913	039
17	2	26	1986	900	793	17	3	26	2014	913	493
17	2	27	1987	901	246	17	3	27	2015	913	946
17	3	0	1988	901	700	18	0	0	2016	914	400

=lbs.	Tons	=kilos.	gms.	=lbs.	Tons	=kilos.	gms.
560	¼	254	012	12,320	5½	5,588	258
1,120	½	508	023	13,440	6	6,096	282
2,240	1	1,016	047	14,560	6½	6,604	305
3,360	1½	1,524	070	15,680	7	7,112	329
4,480	2	2,032	094	16,800	7½	7,620	352
5,600	2½	2,540	117	17,920	8	8,128	376
6,720	3	3,048	141	19,040	8½	8,636	399
7,840	3½	3,556	164	20,160	9	9,144	423
8,960	4	4,064	188	21,280	9½	9,652	446
10,080	4½	4,572	211	22,400	10	10,160	470
11,200	5	5,080	235	24,640	11	11,176	517

LBS. = TONS, CWTS., QRS., & KILOS.

cwt.	qrs.	lbs.	lbs.	=kilos.	gms.	cwt.	qrs.	lbs.	lbs.	=kilos.	gms.
18	0	1	2017	914	854	18	1	1	2045	927	554
18	0	2	2018	915	307	18	1	2	2046	928	007
18	0	3	2019	915	761	18	1	3	2047	928	461
18	0	4	2020	916	214	18	1	4	2048	928	914
18	0	5	2021	916	668	18	1	5	2049	929	368
18	0	6	2022	917	121	18	1	6	2050	929	821
18	0	7	2023	917	575	18	1	7	2051	930	275
18	0	8	2024	918	029	18	1	8	2052	930	729
18	0	9	2025	918	482	18	1	9	2053	931	182
18	0	10	2026	918	936	18	1	10	2054	931	636
18	0	11	2027	919	389	18	1	11	2055	932	089
18	0	12	2028	919	843	18	1	12	2056	932	543
18	0	13	2029	920	296	18	1	13	2057	932	996
18	0	14	2030	920	750	18	1	14	2058	933	450
18	0	15	2031	921	204	18	1	15	2059	933	904
18	0	16	2032	921	657	18	1	16	2060	934	357
18	0	17	2033	922	111	18	1	17	2061	934	811
18	0	18	2034	922	564	18	1	18	2062	935	264
18	0	19	2035	923	018	18	1	19	2063	935	718
18	0	20	2036	923	471	18	1	20	2064	936	171
18	0	21	2037	923	925	18	1	21	2065	936	625
18	0	22	2038	924	379	18	1	22	2066	937	079
18	0	23	2039	924	832	18	1	23	2067	937	532
18	0	24	2040	925	286	18	1	24	2068	937	986
18	0	25	2041	925	739	18	1	25	2069	938	439
18	0	26	2042	926	193	18	1	26	2070	938	893
18	0	27	2043	926	646	18	1	27	2071	939	346
18	1	0	2044	927	100	18	2	0	2072	939	800

T.	c.	q.	lb.	lbs.	=kilos.	gms.	T.	c.	q.	lb.	lbs.	=kilos.	gms.
0	4	1	24	500	226	796	4	9	1	4	10,000	4,535	924
0	8	3	20	1000	453	592	4	18	0	24	11,000	4,989	517
0	13	1	16	1500	680	389	5	7	0	16	12,000	5,443	109
0	17	3	12	2000	907	185	5	16	0	8	13,000	5,896	701
1	6	3	4	3000	1,360	777	6	5	0	0	14,000	6,350	294
1	15	2	24	4000	1,814	370	6	13	3	20	15,000	6,803	886
2	4	2	16	5000	2,267	962	7	2	3	12	16,000	7,257	479
2	13	2	8	6000	2,721	554	7	11	3	4	17,000	7,711	071
3	2	2	0	7000	3,175	147	8	0	2	24	18,000	8,164	663
3	11	1	20	8000	3,628	739	8	9	2	16	19,000	8,618	256
4	0	1	12	9000	4,082	332	8	18	2	8	20,000	9,071	848

cwt.	qrs.	lbs.	lbs.	=kilos.	gms.	cwt.	qrs.	lbs.	lbs.	=kilos.	gms.
18	2	1	2073	940	254	18	3	1	2101	952	954
18	2	2	2074	940	707	18	3	2	2102	953	407
18	2	3	2075	941	161	18	3	3	2103	953	861
18	2	4	2076	941	614	18	3	4	2104	954	314
18	2	5	2077	942	068	18	3	5	2105	954	768
18	2	6	2078	942	521	18	3	6	2106	955	221
18	2	7	2079	942	975	18	3	7	2107	955	675
18	2	8	2080	943	429	18	3	8	2108	956	129
18	2	9	2081	943	882	18	3	9	2109	956	582
18	2	10	2082	944	336	18	3	10	2110	957	036
18	2	11	2083	944	789	18	3	11	2111	957	489
18	2	12	2084	945	243	18	3	12	2112	957	943
18	2	13	2085	945	696	18	3	13	2113	958	396
18	2	14	2086	946	150	18	3	14	2114	958	850
18	2	15	2087	946	604	18	3	15	2115	959	304
18	2	16	2088	947	057	18	3	16	2116	959	757
18	2	17	2089	947	511	18	3	17	2117	960	211
18	2	18	2090	947	964	18	3	18	2118	960	664
18	2	19	2091	948	418	18	3	19	2119	961	118
18	2	20	2092	948	871	18	3	20	2120	961	571
18	2	21	2093	949	325	18	3	21	2121	962	025
18	2	22	2094	949	779	18	3	22	2122	962	479
18	2	23	2095	950	232	18	3	23	2123	962	932
18	2	24	2096	950	686	18	3	24	2124	963	386
18	2	25	2097	951	139	18	3	25	2125	963	839
18	2	26	2098	951	593	18	3	26	2126	964	293
18	2	27	2099	952	046	18	3	27	2127	964	746
18	3	0	2100	952	500	19	0	0	2128	965	200

=lbs.	Tons	=kilos.	gms.	=lbs.	Tons	=kilos.	gms.
560	¼	254	012	12,320	5½	5,588	258
1,120	½	508	023	13,440	6	6,096	282
2,240	1	1,016	047	14,560	6½	6,604	305
3,360	1½	1,524	070	15,680	7	7,112	329
4,480	2	2,032	094	16,800	7½	7,620	352
5,600	2½	2,540	117	17,920	8	8,128	376
6,720	3	3,048	141	19,040	8½	8,636	399
7,840	3½	3,556	164	20,160	9	9,144	423
8,960	4	4,064	188	21,280	9½	9,652	446
10,080	4½	4,572	211	22,400	10	10,160	470
11,200	5	5,080	235	24,640	11	11,176	517

G

cwt.	qrs.	lbs.	lbs.	=kilos.	gms.	cwt.	qrs.	lbs.	lbs.	=kilos.	gms.
19	0	1	2129	965	654	19	1	1	2157	978	354
19	0	2	2130	966	107	19	1	2	2158	978	807
19	0	3	2131	966	561	19	1	3	2159	979	261
19	0	4	2132	967	014	19	1	4	2160	979	714
19	0	5	2133	967	468	19	1	5	2161	980	168
19	0	6	2134	967	921	19	1	6	2162	980	621
19	0	7	2135	968	375	19	1	7	2163	981	075
19	0	8	2136	968	829	19	1	8	2164	981	529
19	0	9	2137	969	282	19	1	9	2165	981	982
19	0	10	2138	969	736	19	1	10	2166	982	436
19	0	11	2139	970	189	19	1	11	2167	982	889
19	0	12	2140	970	643	19	1	12	2168	983	343
19	0	13	2141	971	096	19	1	13	2169	983	796
19	0	14	2142	971	550	19	1	14	2170	984	250
19	0	15	2143	972	004	19	1	15	2171	984	704
19	0	16	2144	972	457	19	1	16	2172	985	157
19	0	17	2145	972	911	19	1	17	2173	985	611
19	0	18	2146	973	364	19	1	18	2174	986	064
19	0	19	2147	973	818	19	1	19	2175	986	518
19	0	20	2148	974	271	19	1	20	2176	986	971
19	0	21	2149	974	725	19	1	21	2177	987	425
19	0	22	2150	975	179	19	1	22	2178	987	879
19	0	23	2151	975	632	19	1	23	2179	988	332
19	0	24	2152	976	086	19	1	24	2180	988	786
19	0	25	2153	976	539	19	1	25	2181	989	239
19	0	26	2154	976	993	19	1	26	2182	989	693
19	0	27	2155	977	446	19	1	27	2183	990	146
19	1	0	2156	977	900	19	2	0	2184	990	600

T.	c.	q.	lb.	lbs.	=kilos.	gms.	T.	c.	q.	lb.	lbs.	=kilos.	gms.
0	4	1	24	500	226	796	4	9	1	4	10,000	4,535	924
0	8	3	20	1000	453	592	4	18	0	24	11,000	4,989	517
0	13	1	16	1500	680	389	5	7	0	16	12,000	5,443	109
0	17	3	12	2000	907	185	5	16	0	8	13,000	5,896	701
1	6	3	4	3000	1,360	777	6	5	0	0	14,000	6,350	294
1	15	2	24	4000	1,814	370	6	13	3	20	15,000	6,803	886
2	4	2	16	5000	2,267	962	7	2	3	12	16,000	7,257	479
2	13	2	8	6000	2,721	554	7	11	3	4	17,000	7,711	071
3	2	2	0	7000	3,175	147	8	0	2	24	18,000	8,164	663
3	11	1	20	8000	3,628	739	8	9	2	16	19,000	8,618	256
4	0	1	12	9000	4,082	332	8	18	2	8	20,000	9,071	848

cwt.	qrs.	lbs.	lbs.	=kilos.	gms.	cwt.	qrs.	lbs.	lbs.	=kilos.	gms.
19	2	1	2185	991	054	19	3	1	2213	1003	754
19	2	2	2186	991	507	19	3	2	2214	1004	207
19	2	3	2187	991	961	19	3	3	2215	1004	661
19	2	4	2188	992	414	19	3	4	2216	1005	114
19	2	5	2189	992	868	19	3	5	2217	1005	568
19	2	6	2190	993	321	19	3	6	2218	1006	021
19	2	7	2191	993	775	19	3	7	2219	1006	475
19	2	8	2192	994	229	19	3	8	2220	1006	929
19	2	9	2193	994	682	19	3	9	2221	1007	382
19	2	10	2194	995	136	19	3	10	2222	1007	836
19	2	11	2195	995	589	19	3	11	2223	1008	289
19	2	12	2196	996	043	19	3	12	2224	1008	743
19	2	13	2197	996	496	19	3	13	2225	1009	196
19	2	14	2198	996	950	19	3	14	2226	1009	650
19	2	15	2199	997	404	19	3	15	2227	1010	104
19	2	16	2200	997	857	19	3	16	2228	1010	557
19	2	17	2201	998	311	19	3	17	2229	1011	011
19	2	18	2202	998	764	19	3	18	2230	1011	464
19	2	19	2203	999	218	19	3	19	2231	1011	918
19	2	20	2204	999	671	19	3	20	2232	1012	371
19	2	21	2205	1000	125	19	3	21	2233	1012	825
19	2	22	2206	1000	579	19	3	22	2234	1013	279
19	2	23	2207	1001	032	19	3	23	2235	1013	732
19	2	24	2208	1001	486	19	3	24	2236	1014	186
19	2	25	2209	1001	939	19	3	25	2237	1014	639
19	2	26	2210	1002	393	19	3	26	2238	1015	093
19	2	27	2211	1002	846	19	3	27	2239	1015	546
19	3	0	2212	1003	300	20	0	0	2240	1016	000

=lbs.	Tons	=kilos.	gms.	=lbs.	Tons	=kilos.	gms.
560	¼	254	012	12,320	5½	5,588	258
1,120	½	508	023	13,440	6	6,096	282
2,240	1	1,016	047	14,560	6½	6,604	305
3,360	1½	1,524	070	15,680	7	7,112	329
4,480	2	2,032	094	16,800	7½	7,620	352
5,600	2½	2,540	117	17,920	8	8,128	376
6,720	3	3,048	141	19,040	8½	8,636	399
7,840	3½	3,556	164	20,160	9	9,144	423
8,960	4	4,064	188	21,280	9½	9,652	446
10,080	4½	4,572	211	22,400	10	10,160	470
11,200	5	5,080	235	24,640	11	11,176	517

Tons	Tnn.	kilos	Tons	Tnn.	kilos	Tons	Tnn.	kilos	Tons	Tnn.	kilos
1	1	016	41	41	656	81	82	296	121	122	936
2	2	032	42	42	672	82	83	312	122	123	952
3	3	048	43	43	688	83	84	328	123	124	968
4	4	064	44	44	704	84	85	344	124	125	984
5	5	080	45	45	720	85	86	360	125	127	000
6	6	096	46	46	736	86	87	376	130	132	080
7	7	112	47	47	752	87	88	392	135	137	160
8	8	128	48	48	768	88	89	408	140	142	240
9	9	144	49	49	784	89	90	424	145	147	320
10	10	160	50	50	800	90	91	440	150	152	400
11	11	176	51	51	816	91	92	456	155	157	480
12	12	192	52	52	832	92	93	472	160	162	560
13	13	208	53	53	848	93	94	488	165	167	640
14	14	224	54	54	864	94	95	504	170	172	720
15	15	240	55	55	880	95	96	520	175	177	800
16	16	256	56	56	896	96	97	536	180	182	880
17	17	272	57	57	912	97	98	552	185	187	960
18	18	288	58	58	928	98	99	568	190	193	040
19	19	304	59	59	944	99	100	584	195	198	120
20	20	320	60	60	960	100	101	600	200	203	200
21	21	336	61	61	976	101	102	616	250	254	000
22	22	352	62	62	992	102	103	632	300	304	800
23	23	368	63	64	008	103	104	648	400	406	400
24	24	384	64	65	024	104	105	664	500	508	000
25	25	400	65	66	040	105	106	680	600	609	600
26	26	416	66	67	056	106	107	696	700	711	200
27	27	432	67	68	072	107	108	712	750	762	000
28	28	448	68	69	088	108	109	728	800	812	800
29	29	464	69	70	104	109	110	744	900	914	400
30	30	480	70	71	120	110	111	760	1000	1016	000
31	31	496	71	72	136	111	112	776	1100	1117	600
32	32	512	72	73	152	112	113	792	1200	1219	200
33	33	528	73	74	168	113	114	808	1300	1320	800
34	34	544	74	75	184	114	115	824	1400	1422	400
35	35	560	75	76	200	115	116	840	1500	1524	000
36	36	576	76	77	216	116	117	856	1600	1625	600
37	37	592	77	78	232	117	118	872	1700	1727	200
38	38	608	78	79	248	118	119	888	1800	1828	800
39	39	624	79	80	264	119	120	904	1900	1930	400
40	40	640	80	81	280	120	121	920	2000	2032	000

Cwts.	=kilos.	gms.
10¼	520	724
½	533	425
¾	546	125
11	558	826
¼	571	526
½	584	227
¾	596	928
12	609	628
¼	622	329
½	635	029
¾	647	730
13	660	431
¼	673	131
½	685	832
¾	698	532
14	711	233
¼	723	933
½	736	634
¾	749	335
15	762	035
¼	774	736
½	787	436
¾	800	137
16	812	838
¼	825	538
½	838	239
¾	850	939
17	863	640
¼	876	341
½	889	041
¾	901	742
18	914	442
¼	927	143
½	939	843
¾	952	544
19	965	245
¼	977	945
½	990	646
¾	1003	346
20	1016	047

Cwts.	=kilos.	gms.
20¼	1028	748
½	1041	448
¾	1054	149
21	1066	849
¼	1079	550
½	1092	251
¾	1104	951
22	1117	652
¼	1130	352
½	1143	053
¾	1155	753
23	1168	454
¼	1181	155
½	1193	855
¾	1206	556
24	1219	256
¼	1231	957
½	1244	658
¾	1257	358
25	1270	059
¼	1282	759
½	1295	460
¾	1308	161
26	1320	861
¼	1333	562
½	1346	262
¾	1358	963
27	1371	663
¼	1384	364
½	1397	065
¾	1409	765
28	1422	466
¼	1435	166
½	1447	867
¾	1460	568
29	1473	268
¼	1485	969
½	1498	669
¾	1511	370
30	1524	071

Cwts.	=kilos.	gms.
30¼	1536	771
½	1549	472
¾	1562	172
31	1574	873
¼	1587	573
½	1600	274
¾	1612	975
32	1625	675
¼	1638	376
½	1651	076
¾	1663	777
33	1676	478
¼	1689	178
½	1701	879
¾	1714	579
34	1727	280
¼	1739	980
½	1752	681
¾	1765	382
35	1778	082
¼	1790	783
½	1803	483
¾	1816	184
36	1828	885
¼	1841	585
½	1854	286
¾	1866	986
37	1879	687
¼	1892	388
½	1905	088
¾	1917	789
38	1930	489
¼	1943	190
½	1955	890
¾	1968	591
39	1981	292
¼	1993	992
½	2006	693
¾	2019	393
40	2032	094

Cwts.	=kilos.	gms.
41	2082	896
42	2133	699
43	2184	501
44	2235	303
45	2286	106
46	2336	908
47	2387	710
48	2438	513
49	2489	315
50	2540	118
51	2590	920
52	2641	722
53	2692	525
54	2743	327
55	2794	129
56	2844	932
57	2895	734
58	2946	536
59	2997	339
60	3048	141
61	3098	943
62	3149	746
63	3200	548
64	3251	350
65	3302	153
66	3352	955
67	3403	757
68	3454	560
69	3505	362
70	3556	165
71	3606	967
72	3657	769
73	3708	572
74	3759	374
75	3810	176
76	3860	979
77	3911	781
78	3962	583
79	4013	386
80	4064	188

7 lb.	3 k. 175 gms.	
14 lb.	6	350
21 lb.	9 k. 525 gms.	

94. @ 1015 kg. SHORT TONS (2000 lb.) = TONNES.

Tons	Tnn.	kilos	Tons	Tnn.	kilos	Tons	Tnn.	kilos	Tons	Tnn.	kilos
1	0	906¼	41	37	156¼	81	73	406¼	121	109	656¼
2	1	812½	42	38	062½	82	74	312½	122	110	562½
3	2	718¾	43	38	968¾	83	75	218¾	123	111	468¾
4	3	625	44	39	875	84	76	125	124	112	375
5	4	531¼	45	40	781¼	85	77	031¼	125	113	281¼
6	5	437½	46	41	687½	86	77	937½	130	117	812½
7	6	343¾	47	42	593¾	87	78	843¾	135	122	343¾
8	7	250	48	43	500	88	79	750	140	126	875
9	8	156¼	49	44	406¼	89	80	656¼	145	131	406¼
10	9	062½	50	45	312½	90	81	562½	150	135	937½
11	9	968¾	51	46	218¾	91	82	468¾	155	140	468¾
12	10	875	52	47	125	92	83	375	160	145	000
13	11	781¼	53	48	031¼	93	84	281¼	165	149	531¼
14	12	687½	54	48	937½	94	85	187½	170	154	062½
15	13	593¾	55	49	843¾	95	86	093¾	175	158	593¾
16	14	500	56	50	750	96	87	000	180	163	125
17	15	406¼	57	51	656¼	97	87	906¼	185	167	656¼
18	16	312½	58	52	562½	98	88	812½	190	172	187½
19	17	218¾	59	53	468¾	99	89	718¾	195	176	718¾
20	18	125	60	54	375	100	90	625	200	181	250
21	19	031¼	61	55	281¼	101	91	531¼	250	226	562½
22	19	937½	62	56	187½	102	92	437½	300	271	875
23	20	843¾	63	57	093¾	103	93	343¾	400	362	500
24	21	750	64	58	000	104	94	250	500	453	125
25	22	656¼	65	58	906¼	105	95	156¼	600	543	750
26	23	562½	66	59	812½	106	96	062½	700	634	375
27	24	468¾	67	60	718¾	107	96	968¾	750	679	687½
28	25	375	68	61	625	108	97	875	800	725	000
29	26	281¼	69	62	531¼	109	98	781¼	900	815	625
30	27	187½	70	63	437½	110	99	687½	1000	906	250
31	28	093¾	71	64	343¾	111	100	593¾	1100	996	875
32	29	000	72	65	250	112	101	500	1200	1087	500
33	29	906¼	73	66	156¼	113	102	406¼	1300	1178	125
34	30	812½	74	67	062½	114	103	312½	1400	1268	750
35	31	718¾	75	67	968¾	115	104	218¾	1500	1359	375
36	32	625	76	68	875	116	105	125	1600	1450	000
37	33	531¼	77	69	781¼	117	106	031¼	1700	1540	625
38	34	437½	78	70	687½	118	106	937½	1800	1631	250
39	35	343¾	79	71	593¾	119	107	843¾	1900	1721	875
40	36	250	80	72	500	120	108	750	2000	1812	500

ctls.	qtls.	kilos	centls.	qtls.	kilos	centls.	qtls.	kilos	centls.	qtls.	kilos
¼	0	11⅜	10¼	4	64½	20¼	9	17⅝	30¼	13	70¾
½	0	22⅝	½	4	75¾	½	9	28⅞	½	13	82
¾	0	34	¾	4	87⅛	¾	9	40¼	¾	13	93⅜
1	0	45⅜	**11**	4	98½	**21**	9	51⅝	**31**	14	04¾
¼	0	56⅝	¼	5	09¾	¼	9	62⅞	¼	14	16
½	0	68	½	5	21⅛	½	9	74¼	½	14	27⅜
¾	0	79¼	¾	5	32⅜	¾	9	85½	¾	14	38⅝
2	0	90⅝	**12**	5	43¾	**22**	9	96⅞	**32**	14	50
¼	1	02	¼	5	55⅛	¼	10	08¼	¼	14	61⅜
½	1	13¼	½	5	66⅜	½	10	19½	½	14	72⅝
¾	1	24⅝	¾	5	77¾	¾	10	30⅞	¾	14	84
3	1	36	**13**	5	89⅛	**23**	10	42¼	**33**	14	95⅜
¼	1	47¼	¼	6	00⅜	¼	10	53½	¼	15	06⅝
½	1	58⅝	½	6	11¾	½	10	64⅞	½	15	18
¾	1	69⅞	¾	6	23	¾	10	76⅛	¾	15	29¼
4	1	81¼	**14**	6	34⅜	**24**	10	87½	**34**	15	40⅝
¼	1	92⅝	¼	6	45¾	¼	10	98⅞	¼	15	52
½	2	03⅞	½	6	57	½	11	10⅛	½	15	63¼
¾	2	15¼	¾	6	68⅜	¾	11	21½	¾	15	74⅝
5	2	26⅝	**15**	6	79¾	**25**	11	32⅞	**35**	15	86
¼	2	37⅞	¼	6	91	¼	11	44⅛	¼	15	97¼
½	2	49¼	½	7	02⅜	½	11	55½	½	16	08⅝
¾	2	60½	¾	7	13⅝	¾	11	66¾	¾	16	19⅞
6	2	71⅞	**16**	7	25	**26**	11	78⅛	**36**	16	31¼
¼	2	83¼	¼	7	36⅜	¼	11	89½	¼	16	42⅝
½	2	94½	½	7	47⅝	½	12	00¾	½	16	53⅞
¾	3	05⅞	¾	7	59	¾	12	12⅛	¾	16	65¼
7	3	17¼	**17**	7	70⅜	**27**	12	23½	**37**	16	76⅝
¼	3	28½	¼	7	81⅝	¼	12	34¾	¼	16	87⅞
½	3	39⅞	½	7	93	½	12	46⅛	½	16	99¼
¾	3	51⅛	¾	8	04¼	¾	12	57⅜	¾	17	10½
8	3	62½	**18**	8	15⅝	**28**	12	68¾	**38**	17	21⅞
¼	3	73⅞	¼	8	27	¼	12	80⅛	¼	17	33¼
½	3	85⅛	½	8	38¼	½	12	91⅜	½	17	44½
¾	3	96½	¾	8	49⅝	¾	13	02¾	¾	17	55⅞
9	4	07⅞	**19**	8	61	**29**	13	14⅛	**39**	17	67¼
¼	4	19⅛	¼	8	72¼	¼	13	25⅜	¼	17	78½
½	4	30½	½	8	83⅝	½	13	36¾	½	17	89⅞
¾	4	41¾	¾	8	94⅞	¾	13	48	¾	18	01⅛
10	4	53⅛	**20**	9	06¼	**30**	13	59⅜	**40**	18	12½

U.S. BUSHELS = HECTOLITRES. @ 35·242 litres.

bush.	hect.	lit.	bush.	hect.	lit.	bush.	hect.	lit.	bush.	hect.	lit.	bush.	hect.	lit.
1	0	35	41	14	45	81	28	55	121	42	64	161	56	74
2	0	70	42	14	80	82	28	90	122	43	00	162	57	09
3	1	06	43	15	15	83	29	25	123	43	35	163	57	44
4	1	41	44	15	51	84	29	60	124	43	70	164	57	80
5	1	76	45	15	86	85	29	96	125	44	05	165	58	15
6	2	11	46	16	21	86	30	31	126	44	40	166	58	50
7	2	47	47	16	56	87	30	66	127	44	76	167	58	85
8	2	82	48	16	92	88	31	01	128	45	11	168	59	21
9	3	17	49	17	27	89	31	37	129	45	46	169	59	56
10	3	52	50	17	62	90	31	72	130	45	81	170	59	91
11	3	88	51	17	97	91	32	07	131	46	17	171	60	26
12	4	23	52	18	33	92	32	42	132	46	52	172	60	62
13	4	58	53	18	68	93	32	78	133	46	87	173	60	97
14	4	93	54	19	03	94	33	13	134	47	22	174	61	32
15	5	29	55	19	38	95	33	48	135	47	58	175	61	67
16	5	64	56	19	74	96	33	83	136	47	93	176	62	03
17	5	99	57	20	09	97	34	18	137	48	28	177	62	38
18	6	34	58	20	44	98	34	54	138	48	63	178	62	73
19	6	70	59	20	79	99	34	89	139	48	99	179	63	08
20	7	05	60	21	15	100	35	24	140	49	34	180	63	44
21	7	40	61	21	50	101	35	59	141	49	69	181	63	79
22	7	75	62	21	85	102	35	95	142	50	04	182	64	14
23	8	11	63	22	20	103	36	30	143	50	40	183	64	49
24	8	46	64	22	55	104	36	65	144	50	75	184	64	85
25	8	81	65	22	91	105	37	00	145	51	10	185	65	20
26	9	16	66	23	26	106	37	36	146	51	45	186	65	55
27	9	52	67	23	61	107	37	71	147	51	81	187	65	90
28	9	87	68	23	96	108	38	06	148	52	16	188	66	25
29	10	22	69	24	32	109	38	41	149	52	51	189	66	61
30	10	57	70	24	67	110	38	77	150	52	86	190	66	96
31	10	93	71	25	02	111	39	12	151	53	22	191	67	31
32	11	28	72	25	37	112	39	47	152	53	57	192	67	66
33	11	63	73	25	73	113	39	82	153	53	92	193	68	02
34	11	98	74	26	08	114	40	18	154	54	27	194	68	37
35	12	33	75	26	43	115	40	53	155	54	63	195	68	72
36	12	69	76	26	78	116	40	88	156	54	98	196	69	07
37	13	04	77	27	14	117	41	23	157	55	33	197	69	43
38	13	39	78	27	49	118	41	59	158	55	68	198	69	78
39	13	74	79	27	84	119	41	94	159	56	03	199	70	13
40	14	10	80	28	19	120	42	29	160	56	39	200	70	48

bush.	hect.	lit.	bush.	hect.	lit.	bush.	hect.	lit.	bush.	hect.	lit.
201	70	84	241	84	93	282	99	38	2200	775	32
202	71	19	242	85	29	284	100	09	2400	845	81
203	71	54	243	85	64	286	100	79	2600	916	29
204	71	89	244	85	99	288	101	50	2800	986	78
205	72	25	245	86	34	290	102	20	3000	1057	26
206	72	60	246	86	70	292	102	91	3200	1127	74
207	72	95	247	87	05	294	103	61	3400	1198	23
208	73	30	248	87	40	296	104	32	3600	1268	71
209	73	66	249	87	75	298	105	02	3800	1339	20
210	74	01	250	88	11	300	105	73	4000	1409	68
211	74	36	251	88	46	310	109	25	4200	1480	16
212	74	71	252	88	81	320	112	77	4400	1550	65
213	75	07	253	89	16	330	116	30	4600	1621	13
214	75	42	254	89	51	340	119	82	4800	1691	62
215	75	77	255	89	87	350	123	35	5000	1762	10
216	76	12	256	90	22	360	126	87	5200	1832	58
217	76	48	257	90	57	380	133	92	5400	1903	07
218	76	83	258	90	92	400	140	97	5600	1973	55
219	77	18	259	91	28	450	158	59	5800	2044	04
220	77	53	260	91	63	500	176	21	6000	2114	52
221	77	88	261	91	98	550	193	83	6200	2185	00
222	78	24	262	92	33	600	211	45	6400	2255	49
223	78	59	263	92	69	650	229	07	6600	2325	97
224	78	94	264	93	04	700	246	69	6800	2396	46
225	79	29	265	93	39	750	264	32	7000	2466	94
226	79	65	266	93	74	800	281	94	7200	2537	42
227	80	00	267	94	10	850	299	56	7400	2607	91
228	80	35	268	94	45	900	317	18	7600	2678	39
229	80	70	269	94	80	950	334	80	7800	2748	88
230	81	06	270	95	15	1000	352	42	8000	2819	36
231	81	41	271	95	51	1200	422	90	8200	2889	84
232	81	76	272	95	86	1400	493	39	8400	2960	33
233	82	11	273	96	21	1500	528	63	8600	3030	81
234	82	47	274	96	56	1600	563	87	8800	3101	30
235	82	82	275	96	92	1800	634	36	9000	3171	78
236	83	17	276	97	27	2000	704	84	9200	3242	26
237	83	52	277	97	62				9400	3312	75
238	83	88	278	97	97				9600	3383	23
239	84	23	279	98	33				9800	3453	72
240	84	58	280	98	68				10000	3524	20

Bsh.	Pks.	Gal.	hect.	lit.
$\frac{1}{4}$	1	2	0	09
$\frac{1}{2}$	2	4	0	18
$\frac{3}{4}$	3	6	0	26

U.S. GALLONS = LITRES & MILLILITRES.

Gal.pt	=litres	millit.	Pints	Gal.pt	=litres	milli.	Pints	Galls.	=litres	milli.	Pints
⅛	0	473	1	5. 1	19	400	41	10¼	38	800	82
¼...	0	946	2	2	19	873	42	½	39	746	84
⅜	1	420	3	3	20	346	43	¾	40	693	86
½...	1	893	4	4	20	820	44	11	41	639	88
⅝	2	366	5	5	21	293	45	¼	42	585	90
¾...	2	839	6	6	21	766	46	½	43	532	92
⅞	3	312	7	7	22	239	47	¾	44	478	94
1. 0	3	785	8	6. 0	22	712	48	12	45	424	96
1	4	259	9	1	23	185	49	¼	46	371	98
2	4	732	10	2	23	659	50	½	47	317	100
3	5	205	11	3	24	132	51	¾	48	263	102
4	5	678	12	4	24	605	52	13	49	210	104
5	6	151	13	5	25	078	53	¼	50	156	106
6	6	624	14	6	25	551	54	½	51	103	108
7	7	098	15	7	26	024	55	¾	52	049	110
2. 0	7	571	16	7. 0	26	498	56	14	52	995	112
1	8	044	17	1	26	971	57	¼	53	942	114
2	8	517	18	2	27	444	58	½	54	888	116
3	8	990	19	3	27	917	59	¾	55	834	118
4	9	463	20	4	28	390	60	15	56	781	120
5	9	937	21	5	28	863	61	½	58	673	124
6	10	410	22	6	29	337	62	16	60	566	128
7	10	883	23	7	29	810	63	½	62	459	132
3. 0	11	356	24	8. 0	30	283	64	17	64	351	136
1	11	829	25	1	30	756	65	½	66	244	140
2	12	302	26	2	31	229	66	18	68	137	144
3	12	776	27	3	31	702	67	½	70	029	148
4	13	249	28	4	32	176	68	19	71	922	152
5	13	722	29	5	32	649	69	½	73	815	156
6	14	195	30	6	33	122	70	20	75	707	160
7	14	668	31	7	33	595	71	21	79	493	168
4. 0	15	141	32	9. 0	34	068	72	22	83	278	176
1	15	615	33	1	34	542	73	23	87	064	184
2	16	088	34	2	35	015	74	24	90	849	192
3	16	561	35	3	35	488	75	25	94	634	200
4	17	034	36	4	35	961	76	26	98	420	208
5	17	507	37	5	36	434	77	27	102	205	216
6	17	981	38	6	36	907	78	28	105	990	224
7	18	454	39	7	37	381	79	29	109	776	232
5. 0	18	927	40	10.0	37	854	80	30	113	561	240

Gall.	=litres	milli.	Galls.	=litres	milli.	Galls.	=litres	milli.	Galls.	=litres	milli.
31	117	346	71	268	761	111	420	176	200	757	074
32	121	132	72	272	547	112	423	961	252	953	913
33	124	917	73	276	332	113	427	747	300	1135	611
34	128	703	74	280	117	114	431	532	400	1514	148
35	132	488	75	283	903	115	435	318	500	1892	685
36	136	273	76	287	688	116	439	103	600	2271	222
37	140	059	77	291	473	117	442	888	700	2649	759
38	143	844	78	295	259	118	446	674	800	3028	296
39	147	629	79	299	044	119	450	459	900	3406	833
40	151	415	80	302	830	120	454	244	1000	3785	370
41	155	200	81	306	615	121	458	030	1100	4163	906
42	158	986	82	310	400	122	461	815	1200	4542	443
43	162	771	83	314	186	123	465	600	1300	4920	980
44	166	556	84	317	971	124	469	386	1400	5299	517
45	170	342	85	321	756	125	473	171	1500	5678	054
46	174	127	86	325	542	126	476	957	1600	6056	591
47	177	912	87	329	327	127	480	742	1700	6435	128
48	181	698	88	333	113	128	484	527	1800	6813	665
49	185	483	89	336	898	129	488	313	1900	7192	202
50	189	268	90	340	683	130	492	098	2000	7570	739
51	193	054	91	344	469	131	495	883	2100	7949	276
52	196	839	92	348	254	132	499	669	2200	8327	813
53	200	625	93	352	039	133	503	454	2300	8706	350
54	204	410	94	355	825	134	507	240	2400	9084	887
55	208	195	95	359	610	135	511	025	2500	9463	424
56	211	981	96	363	396	136	514	810	2600	9841	961
57	215	766	97	367	181	137	518	596	2700	10220	498
58	219	551	98	370	966	138	522	381	2800	10599	035
59	223	337	99	374	752	139	526	166	2900	10977	572
60	227	122	100	378	537	140	529	952	3000	11356	109
61	230	908	101	382	322	141	533	737	3100	11734	645
62	234	693	102	386	108	142	537	523	3200	12113	182
63	238	478	103	389	893	143	541	308	3300	12491	719
64	242	264	104	393	678	144	545	093	3400	12870	256
65	246	049	105	397	464	145	548	879	3500	13248	793
66	249	834	106	401	249	146	552	664	3600	13627	330
67	253	620	107	405	035	147	556	449	3700	14005	867
68	257	405	108	408	820	148	560	235	3800	14384	404
69	261	191	109	412	605	149	564	020	3900	14762	941
70	264	976	110	416	391	150	567	805	4000	15141	478

100. 2240-lb. **TONS** = 2000-lb. **TONS & CENTALS** (100 lb). [1 qr = 25 lb]

tons	=tn. ctls. qr. lbs.	=lbs.	tons	=tn. ctls. qr. lbs.	tons	=tn. ctls. qr. lbs.
1	1 2 1 15	2240	41	45 18 1 15	81	90 14 1 15
2	2 4 3 5	4480	42	47 0 3 5	82	91 16 3 5
3	3 7 0 20	6720	43	48 3 0 20	83	92 19 0 20
4	4 9 2 10	8960	44	49 5 2 10	84	94 1 2 10
5	5 12 0 0	11,200	45	50 8 0 0	85	95 4 0 0
6	6 14 1 15	13,440	46	51 10 1 15	86	96 6 1 15
7	7 16 3 5	15,680	47	52 12 3 5	87	97 8 3 5
8	8 19 0 20	17,920	48	53 15 0 20	88	98 11 0 20
9	10 1 2 10	20,160	49	54 17 2 10	89	99 13 2 10
10	11 4 0 0	22,400	50	56 0 0 0	90	100 16 0 0
11	12 6 1 15	24,640	51	57 2 1 15	91	101 18 1 15
12	13 8 3 5	26,880	52	58 4 3 5	92	103 0 3 5
13	14 11 0 20	29,120	53	59 7 0 20	93	104 3 0 20
14	15 13 2 10	31,360	54	60 9 2 10	94	105 5 2 10
15	16 16 0 0	33,600	55	61 12 0 0	95	106 8 0 0
16	17 18 1 15	35,840	56	62 14 1 15	96	107 10 1 15
17	19 0 3 5	38,080	57	63 16 3 5	97	108 12 3 5
18	20 3 0 20	40,320	58	64 19 0 20	98	109 15 0 20
19	21 5 2 10	42,560	59	66 1 2 10	99	110 17 2 10
20	22 8 0 0	44,800	60	67 4 0 0	100	112 0 0 0
21	23 10 1 15	47,040	61	68 6 1 15	200	224 0 0 0
22	24 12 3 5	49,280	62	69 8 3 5	250	280 0 0 0
23	25 15 0 20	51,520	63	70 11 0 20	300	336 0 0 0
24	26 17 2 10	53,760	64	71 13 2 10	400	448 0 0 0
25	28 0 0 0	56,000	65	72 16 0 0	500	560 0 0 0
26	29 2 0 0	58,240	66	73 18 1 15	600	672 0 0 0
27	30 4 3 5	60,480	67	75 0 3 5	700	784 0 0 0
28	31 7 0 20	62,720	68	76 3 0 20	800	896 0 0 0
29	32 9 2 10	64,960	69	77 5 2 10	900	1008 0 0 0
30	33 12 0 0	67,200	70	78 8 0 0	1000	1120 0 0 0
31	34 14 1 15	69,440	71	79 10 1 15	1100	1232 0 0 0
32	35 16 3 5	71,680	72	80 12 3 5	1200	1344 0 0 0
33	36 19 0 20	73,920	73	81 15 0 20	1300	1456 0 0 0
34	38 1 2 10	76,160	74	82 17 2 10	1400	1568 0 0 0
35	39 4 0 0	78,400	75	84 0 0 0	1500	1680 0 0 0
36	40 6 1 15	80,640	76	85 2 1 15	1600	1792 0 0 0
37	41 8 3 5	82,880	77	86 4 3 5	1700	1904 0 0 0
38	42 11 0 20	85,120	78	87 7 0 20	1800	2016 0 0 0
39	43 13 2 10	87,360	79	88 9 2 10	1900	2128 0 0 0
40	44 16 0 0	89,600	80	89 12 0 0	2000	2240 0 0 0

@ 1015 kg. **TONS (2240 lb.) = TONNES.**

Tons	Tnn.	kilos	Tons	Tnn.	kilos	Tons	Tnn.	kilos	Tons	Tnn.	kilos
1	1	015	41	41	615	81	82	215	121	122	815
2	2	030	42	42	630	82	83	230	122	123	830
3	3	045	43	43	645	83	84	245	123	124	845
4	4	060	44	44	660	84	85	260	124	125	860
5	5	075	45	45	675	85	86	275	125	126	875
6	6	090	46	46	690	86	87	290	130	131	950
7	7	105	47	47	705	87	88	305	135	137	025
8	8	120	48	48	720	88	89	320	140	142	100
9	9	135	49	49	735	89	90	335	145	147	175
10	10	150	50	50	750	90	91	350	150	152	250
11	11	165	51	51	765	91	92	365	155	157	325
12	12	180	52	52	780	92	93	380	160	162	400
13	13	195	53	53	795	93	94	395	165	167	475
14	14	210	54	54	810	94	95	410	170	172	550
15	15	225	55	55	825	95	96	425	175	177	625
16	16	240	56	56	840	96	97	440	180	182	700
17	17	255	57	57	855	97	98	455	185	187	775
18	18	270	58	58	870	98	99	470	190	192	850
19	19	285	59	59	885	99	100	485	195	197	925
20	20	300	60	60	900	100	101	500	200	203	000
21	21	315	61	61	915	101	102	515	250	253	750
22	22	330	62	62	930	102	103	530	300	304	500
23	23	345	63	63	945	103	104	545	400	406	000
24	24	360	64	64	960	104	105	560	500	507	500
25	25	375	65	65	975	105	106	575	600	609	000
26	26	390	66	66	990	106	107	590	700	710	500
27	27	405	67	68	005	107	108	605	750	761	250
28	28	420	68	69	020	108	109	620	800	812	000
29	29	435	69	70	035	109	110	635	900	913	500
30	30	450	70	71	050	110	111	650	1000	1015	000
31	31	465	71	72	065	111	112	665	1100	1116	500
32	32	480	72	73	080	112	113	680	1200	1218	000
33	33	495	73	74	095	113	114	695	1300	1319	500
34	34	510	74	75	110	114	115	710	1400	1421	000
35	35	525	75	76	125	115	116	725	1500	1522	500
36	36	540	76	77	140	116	117	740	1600	1624	000
37	37	555	77	78	155	117	118	755	1700	1725	500
38	38	570	78	79	170	118	119	770	1800	1827	000
39	39	585	79	80	185	119	120	785	1900	1928	500
40	40	600	80	81	200	120	121	800	2000	2030	000